SCIENCE MUSEUM

Broad Gauge

An account of the origins and development of the Great Western
broad gauge system, with a glance at broad gauges in other lands

by Lance Day

London   Her Majesty's Stationery Office

ISBN 0 11 290437 8

Acknowledgements

It is my pleasant task to express my gratitude to a number of people. First, I should like to thank the Director of the Science Museum, Dame Margaret Weston, for encouraging me to write this book. Next, I thank Professor Jack Simmons for, in the first place, suggesting that such a book be produced; I am most grateful to him too for many valuable suggestions in the course of the work and for reading through and correcting the text. I am grateful also to Michael Robbins for reading the section on broad gauges in other countries and for helpful suggestions and corrections.

I gladly acknowledge the help I have received from the staff of the several libraries and record offices where I have consulted original material. Of these, I might single out the Science Museum Library, and in particular Ian Carter who carried out valuable preparatory work. These and others I have not named have saved me from many errors; those that remain are the author's peculiar contribution, for which he takes sole responsibility. Finally, I should like to thank Susan Fishlock, my Secretary, who has grappled successfully with my handwriting to produce for the printer an immaculate typescript.

LRD
September 1984

Broad Gauge

At 5 o'clock on the afternoon of Friday, 20 May 1892, the last broad gauge train moved out of Paddington Station, hauled by one of the legendary 'Iron Duke' class locomotives, and steamed into history. During that weekend, the last purely broad gauge stretch of line was converted to standard gauge, and on the Monday morning, the Great Western for the first time in its history joined the other railways in the country in operating on only standard gauge track. The great broad gauge experiment was over.

Of all the old railway companies, none exerts a greater fascination than the Great Western. It was in so many ways different from other railways, some of the differences surviving to recent times, like the Victorian ornamentation of its steam locomotives. But in no respect was it more distinctive than in the fact that, whereas the other railways in this country, and most overseas railways, were laid with the rails 4 ft 8½ in. apart, the Great Western trod a lone path with rails 7 ft 0¼ in. apart. This was due to the daring imagination of Isambard Kingdom Brunel. Like many of his conceptions, it aroused strong feelings, for and against. The broad gauge protagonists held that their system had great advantages in speed, safety and comfort, whereas their adversaries claimed that the system was an expensive mistake and a gross impediment to the easy working of through traffic in a small, intensively industrialised country. Who were right? The truth, as usual, lies somewhere between the two, and one has to tread carefully to reach a balanced judgement of Brunel's broad gauge system.

Railway gauge had been virtually standardised at 4 ft 8½ in. with the authorisation by Parliament of the first major lines after the opening of the Liverpool & Manchester Railway in September 1830. Before that,[1] railways had been in existence first in German mining districts in the middle ages. They made their appearance in England late in the sixteenth century and by two centuries later there were many short lines of railway in mining areas, ironworks and, later, as feeders to canals. During the latter half of the 18th century, there were also the tramways, but with flanged plate rails on which could run wagons with smooth wheels that would thus also travel on the public roads. But these were a loop line to the main line of railway development. These lines were laid to a variety of gauges, ranging on the whole from 4 ft to 5 ft. Much of the network of railways in the north-east mining area around Newcastle-upon-Tyne was 4 ft 8 in. gauge, a dimension for which there is a tradition stretching back to antiquity, for in Babylon around 3000 BC there were ways laid down consisting of grooves cut in parallel lines of stone blocks. Between the outer edges of the grooves measured 3 cubits, each of 1 ft 8 in., or 5 ft; allowing 2 in. for the width of groove, the inner edges measured 4 ft 8 in. apart. Other ancient examples closely approximating to this figure are known.[2] The reason for this choice of width is not far to seek. It was determined by the width of the average cart horse, which in turn determined the distance between the shafts and also the most effective width of cart.

Parkmoor wagonway, Newcastle upon Tyne, 1783. Detail of an engraving, Science Museum.

Most of the traffic on the early railways was horse-drawn, so 4 ft 8 in. or thereabouts for the north-eastern lines served very well. But this network was the stem from which blossomed the railway development of the nineteenth century. It was here that around 1812 the working of trains of wagons by primitive steam locomotives became increasingly common. The development of this practice was largely due to the skill and determination of the overseer of machinery in a major group of Northumberland collieries, George Stephenson. The locomotives he designed, beginning with the *Blücher* of 1814 were constructed to fit the 4 ft 8 in. gauge of the Killingworth Colliery line and the lines it was connected with. When the Stockton & Darlington line was planned in 1821, with Stephenson as engineer, it was logical to conform to the prevailing gauge. This railway is important as the first public railway to depend largely on steam traction for the movement of goods traffic, but the passenger trains were for a time anyway horse-powered. The rails had therefore to be a horse-width apart and, incidentally, supported on stone blocks rather

than cross sleepers so as not to impede the horses. A different gauge would also have isolated the line from the network in that region. By that time a far more ambitious project was underway, the linking of Liverpool and Manchester by a railway no less than 30 miles in length. After an unfortunate experience at the hands of the Parliamentary Committee examining the Bill for the construction of the railway, the board appointed engineers of the highest standing, the brothers John and George Rennie, to draw up a survey and estimate. They proposed a gauge of 5 ft. But after the passage of the Act, the board was swayed by a pro-Stephenson faction, and George Rennie's offer to act as engineer for the construction of the line was turned down. Stephenson found himself in charge and in July 1826, with his advice and little discussion, it was resolved that 'the width of the Waggon Way between the rails be the same as on the Darlington Road, namely 4 ft 8 in. clear inside the rails'. The firm of Robert Stephenson & Co. Ltd. had been established in 1823 in Newcastle, the first set up to manufacture steam locomotives, to supply machines for the north-east, and the Stockton & Darlington in particular, and they expected to provide locomotives for the Liverpool & Manchester as well. It would be convenient if they could be constructed to the same gauge; they could then be tested on the lines around Newcastle before delivery. That seems to have been the main consideration, although this firm later built locomotives for various gauges, to order. But the Liverpool & Manchester track seems to have been made to fit the locomotives.[3]

The railway was opened on 15 September 1830, one of the wonders of the world and an outstanding success in every way. The event marked a watershed in human history, for it inaugurated a revolution in transport, with wide-ranging social and economic effects in this country and throughout the world. An immediate result was a spate of more ambitious projects for railway construction. In particular in 1833, both the Grand Junction Railway, connecting the Liverpool & Manchester line to Birmingham, and the London & Birmingham Railway were authorised. The three lines joined the most important industrial centres with the capital and clearly all had to be of the same gauge – 4 ft 8 in. At this time the wheels of the rolling stock were given a little extra freedom, and a half inch was added to the gauge and has remained ever since, although in 1964 the standard was set at 1432 mm (4 ft 8½ in. is 1435 mm).

After the opening drama, the Liverpool & Manchester settled down to steady operation. Towards the end of 1831, on 5 December, a small dark young man of 25 armed with a notebook took train at Manchester bound for Liverpool. It was Isambard Kingdom Brunel, on a tour of the north, looking at various engineering projects and hoping for a commission worthy of his talents. Since his father's great work on the Thames Tunnel had come to a halt due to flooding and shortage of funds, Brunel had been rather at a loose end. A number of schemes had come to nothing and his attempts from early 1830 to gain a footing in the railway projects then gathering pace had failed. Mid–1832 found his spirits at a low ebb, with so much going on around him, in which he was having so little part. But two projects at

Isambard Kingdom Brunel. Painting by J.C. Horsley, dated 1857, but probably showing Brunel as he appeared in his early forties. Courtesy of the National Portrait Gallery.

Bristol, the designing of a suspension bridge over the Avon Gorge at Clifton and important dock works, forged a Bristol connection that was to be instrumental in providing him with his great opportunity – the building of a railway between Bristol and London.

The diary entry for the day of his first railway journey is in some ways prophetic. On an interleaved sheet of paper, he drew some wavering circles and lines, and wrote: 'Drawn on the L&M railway 5.12.31. I record this specimen of the shaking on the Manchester railway. The time is not far off when we shall be able to take our coffee and write while going noiselessly and smoothly at 45 miles per hour – let me try!' Early in 1833, someone did let him try.[4]

The merchants of Bristol were greatly concerned that their city had slipped from the proud position as England's premier provincial port, having lately been overtaken by Liverpool. A group of the leading merchants initiated a series of improvements in the dock and harbour arrangements and then turned their attention to communications. Several proposals had already been put forward for a railway to London, one as early as 1824, but had led to nothing. Now, with the success of the Liverpool & Manchester pointing the way, in the autumn of 1832 a group of four merchants met in a dingy office in the heart of Bristol to resurrect this idea. They enlisted support to such effect that before the end of the year an organising committee had been set up, including representatives of the five corporate bodies of Bristol. Early in the following year they agreed to pay for a preliminary survey of the route to London and an estimate of the cost. A sub-committee was appointed to pursue this and select an engineer to carry out the survey. There were four contenders, including Brunel. The committee thought it reasonable to accept the lowest estimate but Brunel would have none of that. He fulminated: 'You are holding out a premium to the man who will make you the most flattering promises, and it is quite obvious that he who has the least reputation at stake, or the most to gain by temporary success, and least to lose by the consequences of a disappointment, must be the winner in such a race'. He would agree to survey just one route and that would be the best, not the cheapest. By one vote, the committee agreed to appoint him, and on 7 March 1833 he found himself in charge of what he afterwards called the 'finest work in England'. By this slender margin was reached a decision momentous for Brunel's career and the future of British railway development.[5]

Brunel immediately set about his work with furious energy and relentless drive. His assistant was a local surveyor, W.H. Townsend, who had surveyed a line from Bristol to Gloucester and was in charge of its construction. He had been a contender for the post on the line to London; Brunel was not impressed: 'How the devil I am to get on

with him tied to my neck, I know not!' To complete the survey in good time meant punishing hours and incessant travelling, by Brunel anyway, and the fee of £500 was well earned. Brunel's diary entries for this period show not only his capacity for hard work but his attention to detail, which he was reluctant to delegate to assistants, not always with good reason.

They inspected two routes between Bath and Reading, one north of the Marlborough Downs, through Swindon and the Vale of the White Horse, while the other led through Bradford, Devizes and Newbury, but strongly recommended the former. Several routes east of Maidenhead were surveyed and the point at which the line would strike the metropolis was as yet to be determined. In May, the survey and estimate were complete and delivered to the Committee. The cost of constructing the 118-mile line was estimated at £2 805 330, or at an average per mile of £23 774. This compares with the estimate of £2 500 000 for the London to Birmingham line of 112 miles length or £22 321 per mile.[6] The major work on both was tunnelling through the same range of limestone hills, at Box and Kilsby respectively.

There is no hint in the survey that Brunel had in mind a gauge different from the 4 ft 8½ in. to which other lines were being constructed at the time. Nevertheless, according to his own account, the idea must already have occurred to him. In the report of 15 September 1835 to the Directors of the Great Western Railway Company, in which he formally proposed the broad bauge, he asserts that the additional cost of construction 'has been provided for in the estimate'. His first report to the Board, dated a day earlier, states 'It is known to some of the Directors that I have always contemplated a wider gauge for the purpose of using broader carriages and larger wheels'. But if that was his thinking, back in 1833, there is no evidence that broad gauge went beyond the confines of his mind.

Armed with the survey and estimate, the Committee convened a public meeting on 30 July and it was there agreed that a company be formed to establish railway communication between Bristol and London. Separate committees were appointed, of directors in Bristol and

London. The first joint meeting of the two took place on 22 August, adjourned to 27 August, and it was decided that the railway should be called the *Great* Western Railway, the first of many railways to enhance their dignity with this epithet. Brunel now had the task of conducting a detailed survey, required not only for the construction of the line but for Parliament to examine before it could be authorised. Meanwhile, members of the Board, but above all the Secretary, Charles Saunders, worked tirelessly to raise half the stated capital of £3 million that Parliament's standing orders insisted on before the Bill could go ahead. By October, only a quarter had been subscribed and rather than miss the current session of Parliament, it was decided to scale down the initial Bill and seek authorisation of only the London to Reading and Bath to Bristol stretches. But Brunel had a tough time of it: 'It is harder work than I like. I am rarely much under twenty hours a day at it'. The detailed survey was completed and the plans deposited at the end of November, for a route deviating little from the existing line, except at the London end and at a few other points. The Bill passed through the House of Commons in July 1834, after a Committee stage of no less than 57 days, during which Brunel acquitted himself well under examination, to the admiration of George Stephenson, among others. But the House of Lords was less amenable. The truncated scheme was slated as neither great, nor western, nor even much of a railway, and it was thrown out. The Bill[7] omitted the usual clause specifying that the gauge should be 4 ft 8 in., as did the London & Southampton Railway Act in the same session. It must be significant that the Great Western Bill stipulated that the width of land was not to exceed 22 yards whereas the London & Birmingham and Grand Junction Acts had specified 20 yards. (The first railway act that at least implied a non-standard gauge was that of the Cheltenham & Great Western Union Railway, which received the Royal Assent on 21 June 1836. Clause 101 stipulated that 'the track between Cheltenham and Gloucester should be so constructed that Birmingham and Gloucester [i.e. narrow gauge] trains can use them'.)

It was too late to bring in a fresh Bill in the 1833–4 session so the Board began to prepare for the next one. Valuable experience had been gained and the delay enabled the Company to raise sufficient capital for them to bring in a bill for the whole line. Undaunted they drew up a supplementary prospectus, issued in September, definitely proposing that the line should pass through Slough, Maidenhead, Reading, Swindon, Chippenham and Bath. This route was preferred because of its level grades, which could allow the most economical working with steam locomotives, and also it could more readily provide access, by means of branches, to Oxford, Cheltenham and Gloucester, and South Wales. The other possible route, through Hungerford, Devizes and Bradford, was decidedly inferior on other accounts. The estimated cost of construction was £2 500 000, or £305 330 less than the original one, due mainly to a change of route near London, but also because Brunel had been able to make a more precise estimate. The point of arrival in London had still not been fixed, but the Great Western were negotiating with the London & Birmingham Company for a junction with their line near Wormwood Scrubs and sharing their line into the station at Euston. This route appeared in the new edition of the prospectus in November 1834. By the end of the following February, the promoters had succeeded in raising the capital required by Parliament, for 10 000 shares of £100 had been taken up, making a capital, with the previous 10 000, of £2 million.

The way was clear for the second Great Western Railway Bill. It passed its second reading on 9 March 1835 and entered the Committee stage, under the chairmanship of Charles Russell, MP for Reading. Russell was to become a powerful friend of the Great Western and he made short work of the opposition to the Bill. The main opposition came from the London & Southampton Railway, having only lately received their Act. They had thoughts of striking out from Basingstoke in the direction of Bristol and seized on the proposed tunnel at Box as an insuperable objection to Brunel's line. The reasons make amusing reading, Dr. Dionysius Lardner, the noted popularizer of science, providing, as on other occasions, much of the comedy. The tunnel was on a gradient of 1 in 100 and Lardner warned that if the brakes failed, a train would hurtle down at

120 mph, with disastrous consequences. Brunel had only to point out that the learned gentleman had forgotten the restraining effects of friction and air resistance, which would keep the speed down to 56 mph. This seems an easy point for Brunel to score, but 56 mph was still sufficiently alarming, and far above the speed that was first permitted in ordinary running. Brunel had thought to forestall criticism of this sharp incline by consulting George Stephenson and H.R. Palmer; they decisively recommended a level road with a short, sharp incline, rather than a longer, more gradual rise. Based on the known capacity of the locomotives then in use, the general policy was to make a route as level as possible, and concentrate rises in short stretches where the locomotive could be assisted by a second locomotive or a rope worked by a stationary engine.

The London & Southampton defended their hillier route by claiming that the rises and falls would cancel each other out, rendering the line practically level. The Chairman drily remarked that on that principle the Highlands of Scotland would be an ideal area for railway construction.

Under Russell's guidance, the Committee found in favour of the Bill, and it passed its third reading on 26 May. Its passage through the Lords, opposed on much the same grounds as in the Commons, was achieved in August, and it received the Royal Assent on the last day of August, 1835.[8] The Great Western Railway was thereby incorporated and empowered to construct a railway between London and Bristol, with branches to Bradford and Trowbridge.

The new Company held its first general meeting on 29 October and resolved to press ahead with construction, first of the London to Maidenhead and Bristol to Bath sections. But before that, Brunel had launched on the Directors his bombshell of 15 September,[9] urging his case for the broad gauge. In giving evidence to the Gauge Commissioners of 1845, he said that he could not remember just when he had determined on a wider gauge than 4 ft 8½ in. 'Looking to the speeds which I contemplated could be adopted on railways and the masses to be moved, it seemed to me that the whole machine was too small for the work to be done, and that it required that the parts should be on a scale more commensurate with the mass and the velocity to be attained. I think the impression grew upon me gradually, so that it is difficult to fix the time when I first thought a wide gauge desirable; but I daresay there were stages between wishing that it could be so and determining to try to do it.' Brunel, according to his own account, made representations to Lord Shaftesbury, Chairman of Committee in the House of Lords, persuading him to omit the gauge clause from the Great Western Bill. How much wider the gauge should be Brunel seems not to have determined until after the Act was passed, for in evidence to the House of Lords Committee on 23 June, he stated that the tunnels would be 25 ft wide, whereas they were made 30 ft wide to accommodate the broad gauge. It was in his 15 September report that the 7 ft gauge burst upon the scene.

Brunel argued that over most of the proposed line, the resistance to the motion of the carriages due to friction would far outweigh that due to gravity. The former was 9 or even 8 lb per ton, whereas with the line rising for much of its length at no more than 4 ft per mile, the resistance due to gravity would not exceed 2 lb a ton. It therefore made sense to reduce the friction, which could be lowered proportionately by increasing the diameter of the carriage wheels. But reasonably sized carriages and wagons on the narrow gauge had to be placed above and overhang the wheels, thus limiting their size. This meant that the centre of gravity was higher than it need have been, tending to produce unstable running. With the imperfect track and vehicles with short wheelbase and less than adequate suspension, violent oscillations in motion were then a problem, and engineers were concerned to minimise these effects by keeping the centre of gravity as low as possible. Brunel proposed to do this by lowering the carriage body between the wheels, which could then be made as large as necessary to reduce resistance due to friction. Brunel did not immediately suggest that the wheel diameter be greatly increased, but he wanted to provide for it: 'my great object would be in every possible way to render each part capable of improvement, and to remove what appears to be an obstacle to any great progress in such a very important point as the diameter of the wheels which the resistance, which governs the cost of transport and the speed that may be obtained, so materially depends'.

Brunel then tried to meet the four objections he foresaw might be brought against the 7 ft gauge, namely, increased expense in constructing the line and all the works, the greater amount of friction on curves, the additional weight of the carriages and the difficulties at the proposed junction with the London & Birmingham Railway.

Since in Brunel's mind the carriages would be the same width as on standard gauge lines, the total width of the railway would be very little greater. The additional cost of the earthworks in cuttings and embankments, and of bridges and tunnels would only be one twelfth, which, he said, had been allowed for in the original estimate. Similarly, the only larger parts of the carriages would be the axles and, eventually, the wheels, and even this additional weight could be offset by improvements in frame design.

The friction between the wheel flanges and the rails on curves would be increased in proportion to the gauge, about 5 to 7, but Brunel had surveyed a route with very gentle curves, with the avowed aim of minimising friction, and this would only be noticeable in the sharper curves at main stations, where speed would in any case be low.

That left the difficulties at the junction with the London & Birmingham. Brunel thought these could be overcome by laying a third rail, provided that could be agreed. In fact, negotiations broke down on other grounds and so this objection was removed.

Brunel's powers of persuasion, with the spoken and written word, were considerable, as his performance before parliamentary committees had demonstrated, and on 29 October 1835 the Directors accepted their engineer's recommendation. The decision was first published in the Company's report to the half-yearly meeting at Bristol in the following August, although it had become widely known before that. The report suggests that there had been misgivings about the ability of manufacturers to construct locomotives for the wider gauge, but 'the Directors have pleasure in stating that several of the most experienced and eminent manufacturers of Locomotive Engines in the North have undertaken to construct them. They were expected to

Blisworth cutting on the London & Birmingham Railway showing stone block track. Lithograph in J.C. Bourne, *Drawings of the London & Birmingham Railway*, 1839.

attain 35 to 40 mph with the same ease as locomotives achieved 25 to 30 in other lines.'

Meanwhile construction of the line had started from the London and Bristol ends, their respective committees letting contracts independently of each other, while Brunel darted between the two, keeping the details of the work under close personal supervision.

Brunel had devised not only a new gauge but a new method of supporting the track.[10] Most of the lines then under construction or completed were laid with solid section wrought iron rails, twelve to fifteen feet in length, supported at intervals in iron chairs fastened either to wooden cross sleepers or to stone blocks. The London & Birmingham line was using stone blocks, 18 in. by 14 in. by 8 in., weighing about 30 lb. Wooden sleepers laid down in their natural state had on average a life of 7 years, whereas stone blocks lasted much longer and gave a firmer support to the rails. They were, however, subject to varying degrees of settlement and adjusting the blocks to provide a level road was an expensive and lengthy affair. An observer noted that 'a large force must be maintained to preserve the road in sufficient order for the passage of the engines. Directly as

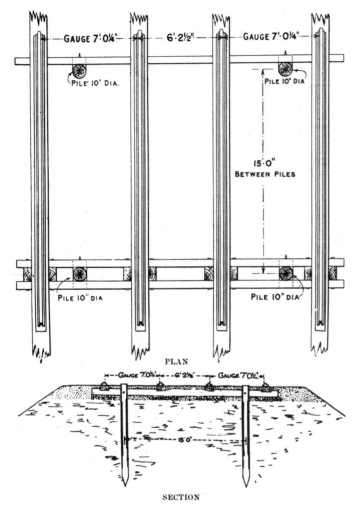

GAUGE 7'·0¼" — 6'·2½" — GAUGE 7'·0¼"

PILE 10" DIA.

PILE 10" DIA

15'·0" BETWEEN PILES

PILE 10" DIA

PILE 10" DIA

PLAN

GAUGE 7'0¼" — 6'2½" — GAUGE 7'0¼"

15'0"

SECTION

Brunel's original permanent way, 1838. E.T. MacDermot, *History of the Great Western Railway*, vol. 1, 1927.

These timbers, 30 ft in length and measuring 12 to 14 inches breadth by 5 to 7 inches depth, were placed along the whole line. These were bolted to cross sleepers or transoms laid at 15 ft intervals; double transoms about 24 ft long and spanning the width of the double track were laid under the joints of the longitudinal timbers, single transoms in between. To give a firm support, sand or gravel was rammed under the timbers, tending to force them upwards. To hold them down two piles were driven into the ground and bolted to each transom. It was this device of pegging down the timber frame by means of piles that was Brunel's particular contribution. The rails too were different. Other lines used solid section rails weighing some 60 lb per yard. Brunel thought he could achieve, with his continuous timbers, lightness combined with adequate strength by using a rail of inverted U-section, known as bridge rails, and weighing only 43 lb a yard. The rails were actually laid 7 ft 0¼ in. apart although it was always referred to as 7 ft.

To lengthen the life of the timbers, Brunel had them subjected to the recently introduced preservation process known as kyanising.[12] This consisted of steeping the wood for 8 days in a solution of corrosive sublimate (mercuric chloride). The method was occasionally used in the 18th century but it was the patent of 1832 by John Howard Kyan that drew attention to it and its commercial application followed on. Tests made on samples of the Great Western timbers six years after they were laid showed they were 'as sound as on the day on which they were first put down'. After 1840, however, in countries possessing sufficient coal to produce adequate quantities of creosote by distillation, kyanising was gradually superseded.

The new method of construction proved more laborious and time-consuming than expected and bad weather and difficulties with the supply of materials further held up the work. Introducing so many novelties, Brunel ran the risk of criticism if things went wrong and in his report to the Directors of 26 January 1837, he defended his methods, pointing out that the estimated additional cost of £500 a mile over that of the established method of construction would be recovered in a few years by cheaper maintenance. He claimed indeed that the higher prices the London &

the train passes, a gang of workmen appears, whose task it is to raise and adjust the blocks over which the engine has just passed; lest the succeeding train be thrown off the track'. Brunel therefore revived the earlier method of longitudinal timber bearings, giving continuous support to the rail.

Birmingham were paying for rails and stone blocks might even extinguish the cost difference.[13]

Eventually, on 31 May 1838, the first section from a temporary terminus at Paddington to Maidenhead (i.e. Taplow), just over 22 miles, was ready for inauguration, and the public service began on Whit Monday, 4 June.

The Times[14] reported that the event 'secured an influx of holidaymakers and formed an era in the recollections of Cockneys, reminding them of pleasure and enjoyment'. Many came for the ride but others used the new line to attend the Eton Montem festival. The report confirmed that observers had found during trials on various stretches of the line before opening, that 'nothing can be more easy than the motion'. But not everyone was satisfied. The proprietors, inspired by Brunel, had made large claims for the superiority of the Great Western over other railways and when practice fell short of the claim, voices were raised in criticism. True, the ride was quieter than on the London & Birmingham, for example, and there was less side-to side oscillation of the carriage, but there was what was called 'uneasiness' in the motion. This appears to have been a pitching or up and down movement and was due to settlement of the longitudinal timbers, or imperfect packing under them, in between the transoms that were held up by the piles. So these became a 'series of props instead of holding-down pins'.[15] Sometimes the riding was downright rough because of defects in the springing of some of the carriages. Nevertheless, informed commentators were forebearing; some teething troubles were to be expected with a new and otherwise promising system, before the new track had time to settle down.[16]

The locomotives, although they had performed impressively on test, were disappointing in regular service. Brunel was not simply constructing a railway line, he had conceived a whole new railway system, on a grand scale, down to the last detail, and the design of the locomotives was an integral part of his scheme. Arguing from mechanical principles rather than established practice, he specified very large driving wheels, to combine high speed with low piston speeds and thus low wear and tear; there were other unusual features. The newly appointed 'Superintendent of Locomotive Engines', Daniel Gooch, took a less sanguine view of these machines. 'I went to inspect the engines building. I was not much pleased with the design of the engines ordered; they had very small boilers and cylinders, and very large wheels.'[17] Gooch had been engaged by Brunel as locomotive engineer the preceding August, just a week before his 21st birthday.

Gooch had been trained in the Stephenson tradition and while working at the works of Robert Stephenson & Co. encountered a gauge wider than 4 ft 8½ in. Two of the locomotives he worked on there were ordered for the New Orleans Railway, USA, built to the 5 ft 6 in. gauge. The order fell through and was taken up by the Great Western, the locomotives being modified to their 7 ft gauge; one of them was the *North Star*, one of the most famous names in British railway history. Gooch records how impressed he was by the wide gauge as it greatly eased the task of laying out the mechanism between the frames. The first locomotives to work on the Liverpool & Manchester had outside cylinders, on the pattern of Stephenson's *Rocket*, but it was soon found, particularly with their short wheelbase, that cylinders placed between the frames and so with the reciprocating forces working near the centre line of the locomotive, produced a steadier running machine. This necessitated a double crank in the driving axle together with the mechanism for actuating the valves that admitted steam to the cylinders and allowed its exit. By the late 1830s, this valve gear had become more elaborate, requiring the use of two pairs of eccentrics, also working on the single driving axle. In 1838, when the railway gauge became a debatable issue, locomotive builders, when asked, usually said they could have done with the extra room between the frames that a wider gauge would have allowed.

Meanwhile, Gooch was hard at work trying to keep his ill-assorted locomotives serviceable. On the second day of the public service, *The Times*[18] reported a large crowd present at Paddington, awaiting the arrival of the train from Maidenhead due at 8 pm, but at 9 pm it had still not put in an appearance. They were 'desperately anxious' lest some fearful accident had befallen it, but soon after 9, it hove in sight. The *Apollo* locomotive had burst a pipe soon after leaving Maidenhead and there was a delay of an hour before it was fit to proceed on its journey. The following train had a narrow escape. The guards noticed a dirt truck on the line in the path of the train; they 'called the engineer', who applied the brakes and managed to avert a disaster. These were the normal hazards of railway travel in the 1830s. They did not deter the public from using the railway and receipts rose steadily over the first months of operation. A comparison of receipts per day per mile of route open taken in June of that year shows the Great Western well up in the table, at £10 2s 8d, only exceeded by the Liverpool & Manchester with £11 0s 2d. The Grand Junction, London & Birmingham and London & Southampson mustered around £5 to £6.[19] But not everyone was satisfied. A group of shareholders from the north, the land of Stephenson, were convinced that the line was costing far more to construct than estimated and this was attributed to the untried novelties introduced by Brunel. The wonderful advantages promised by their engineer had not materialised; instead of swift, smooth travel they were being fobbed off with a rough ride, although one of the directors, George Henry Gibbs, took a journey on the London & Birmingham and found the running just as bad. But the shareholders were promised something much better and the Lancashire investors centred their animosity on the broad gauge and on Brunel, although Gibbs accused them of deeper designs: 'The present outcry . . . has much less to do with the deficiencies of our rails than with the machinations of the party which has long been trying to crush Brunel and to get a share in the management of our line'. Beginning with the shareholders' meeting on 15 August 1838 a move was made to oust Brunel. 'Poor fellow' wrote Gibbs, 'I pity him exceedingly, and I know not how he will get through the storm'.

Even the directors were divided, some advocating the appointment of a second engineer to act jointly with Brunel. This was tantamount to driving him out of his position. The Board invited eminent engineers to inspect the system of construction and make recommendations. Robert Stephenson, James Walker, President of the Institution of Civil Engineers, and Nicholas Wood were invited but only Wood accepted. John Hawkshaw, twenty-seven year old engineer of the Manchester & Leeds Railway, agreed also to examine and report, independently of Wood. This was early in September, and with a storm blowing up, they had a matter of weeks only to make an exhaustive and critical examination and come to a rational conclusion as to whether the broad gauge system should be carried on for the rest of the line to Bristol or be abandoned in favour of the 'Stephenson' system of narrow gauge track on stone blocks – all that in a field in which practice norms could hardly be said to have been established and in which it was still not very clear how mechanical theory could determine practical designs.

Hawkshaw reported first,[20] pointing out straight away that 'any company deviating from this [4 ft 8½ in.) guage will be isolating themselves to a certain extent'. (The word was at first variously spelt until it settled down to 'gauge'.) Apart from that he condemned the 7 ft system on financial grounds and showed that it would pay the Great Western to convert the existing length to narrow gauge, at an estimated cost of £123 976 and save £156 000 on the construction of the remaining length.

Brunel made short work of these calculations. He had maintained all along that the total width of earthworks and structures need be little if at all greater for the broad gauge. He estimated the saving in land purchase for narrow gauge at £50 a mile. The saving in the construction of the permanent way was merely 'the cost of a few cubic feet of ballast per yard and about eight loads of timber to the mile in transoms', the rails and longitudinal timber bearings, of course, remaining the same. The saving thus came down from £1000 to £150 a mile. Next, Brunel claimed that the only additional expense in constructing broad gauge locomotives was that of longer axles and wider frames, or £150 an engine at most; he had no idea of increasing the size of the boiler, cylinders or motion on account of the wider gauge. Finally, Brunel maintained that 30 ft was the proper width for a tunnel, citing narrow gauge tunnels that were constructed to around that figure. So there was no saving to be claimed on that score. The rival claims by Hawkshaw and Brunel can be summarised as follows:

	Hawkshaw	Brunel
Saving of £1000 per mile on permanent way (rails and supports) over 100 miles	£100 000	£15 000
Saving on locomotives and tenders yet to be constructed	24 000	9 000
Saving of £200 per mile on earthwork yet to be completed (60 miles)	12 000	15 000
Saving of 20% on tunnelling by reducing the tunnel widths by 4 ft, say 2000 yards at £10 a yard	20 000	nil
	156 000	39 000

Brunel's comments upon the evils likely to befall on building lines to different gauges seem extraordinary and they were proved erroneous within half a dozen years, but he was not alone in thinking that the Great Western was opening up for railway communication a new and completely self-contained area. He admitted that a break of gauge would be an 'inconvenience', and would have to be ruled out on the lines from London to the north, as they depended for their traffic upon connections with existing narrow gauge lines. But the Great Western 'broke ground in an entirely new district, in which railways were unknown'. The main line and its branches would have a monopoly in the west of England and South Wales. The branches could have no connection with any other main line, 'nor can these be dependent upon any other existing lines for the traffic which they will bring to the main trunk.' 'The Great Western was therefore free to adopt its own dimensions; and none of the difficulties which would entirely prevent such a course in the north of England had any existence in the west'.

The *Railway Magazine* commented: 'Mr. Hawkshaw has been very unfortunate in several of his data and calculations; and his conclusion to bring back the Great Western gage – not to a gage greater than the old, which all

his own authorities admit is not wide enough, – but to that gage which all declare to be too narrow, is the strongest condemnation of his judgement that could be given'.

Brunel was able to pick holes in Hawkshaw's report quite easily; it had after all been dated 4 October, hardly a month after the letter inviting him to report, dated 5 September. Nicholas Wood, on the other hand, carried out a more elaborate investigation, devising experiments to test the broad gauge claims to greater speed, greater mechanical advantage due to lower friction, and greater firmness of the track. Wood could not attend personally to all this testing; some was devolved upon Dr. Dionysius Lardner. The first extended series of comparative tests of efficiency, that is, performance related to fuel consumption, were attempted, comparing results of Great Western locomotives with those of the London & Birmingham and Liverpool & Manchester. Wood found that narrow gauge locomotives could perform, that is, haul the same loads at the same speeds as on the Great Western, but with a lower consumption of coke. From his measurement of the effects of air resistance, which increased rapidly as the square of the speed, he concluded that 35 miles an hour was the highest that could be expected with passenger trains, 'with existing engine powers' and that it was not necessary to go to the expense of widening the gauge to achieve that. However, if Great Western locomotives and carriages were to be improved, further investigation might show a greater advantage for the broad gauge. Meanwhile, the arguments against it were not strong enough to justify the great cost of modifying what had so far been constructed.

It could have been worse, but it was not the unqualified commendation Brunel had been looking for, to sway the shareholders hungry for his blood. The *Railway Magazine* observed: 'On the whole this report presents some valuable information, but comes to nothing very decisive'. One piece of information that was to assume crucial importance concerned the performance of the *North Star* locomotive. The test runs made by Lardner and included by Wood in his report showed that, in order to achieve 41 mph, the load had to be reduced to 16 tons, while the coke consumption shot up to 2.76 lb per ton (hauled) per mile. This inferior

North Star locomotive, 1837. Science Museum scale drawing.

result was attributed to the greater air resistance encountered by the larger front of a broad gauge engine, and was very damaging to Brunel's case. So Brunel and Gooch conducted experiments of their own. It seemed that *North Star* could not get rid of its exhaust steam fast enough and that it was throttling itself. Gooch enlarged the blast pipe and placed it in the smoke box so that 'the steam was discharged up the middle of the chimney'.[21] The improvement seemed extraordinary. *North Star* attained 40 miles an hour hauling 40 tons, but now consuming a mere 0.95 lb of coke per ton/mile. She repeated this performance on a demonstration run staged for the edification and encouragement of some of the directors. It saved the day. Brunel, in his reply to Wood, felt able to discount everything that had been based on inferior broad gauge performance, and the directors went into the adjourned shareholders' meeting on 9 January 1839 with confidence in their engineer and his system. They rallied support and overcame the Lancashire Party. The directors'

recommendations that the piling should be discontinued, that the longitudinal timbers be enlarged and a heavier rail, weighing 62 lb a mile, be used and that the 7 ft gauge be retained, were carried by 7790 votes to 6145, including many proxy votes. This was the end of the opposition to Brunel and the broad gauge.

The railway press, although strongly in support of Brunel, was sceptical that what amounted to an 800 per cent improvement had been achieved 'by knocking the end off a pipe'.[22] Taking account of the weight of the engine and tender and of air resistance, the performance itself could be shown to be only about 25 per cent better. The coke consumption should have been related to the power output ('gross duty') of the engine. It also emerged that Wood had noted a *North Star* effort in which a load of 41.65 tons had been pulled at 39 mph, consuming 1.09 lb of coke per ton/mile, a result similar to but a little inferior to Gooch's result. Wood was severely taken to task for apparently deliberately concealing this observation; the comparison of this run with Gooch's had the advantage of credibility, although it would have been much less dramatic and useful in swaying unconcinved shareholders than the previous comparison.

Brunel had survived the storm and was able to devote himself without distraction and anxiety to the completion of the line. Immediately beyond the first stretch of line to be opened came one of the major works, the bridge over the Thames at Maidenhead. Under the conditions imposed by the Thames Commissioners, Brunel was limited to only one supporting pier in a 300 ft length. That meant two spans of 128 ft and, at the level at which he was bringing in the track, there was an arch rise of a mere 24 ft 3 in. The result was a typically daring Brunel conception, two of the largest and flattest brick arches ever to be constructed. His critics confidently expected the bridge to collapse when the timber centerings were removed, and these fears were not groundless, for when the young John Fowler (later *Sir John*, one of the engineers responsible for the Forth Bridge 50 years later) visited the works in May 1838, he found the

bridge 'I am sorry to say, in a dangerous situation'. The contractor had eased the centering before the cement had properly set and three courses of bricks near the crown of the eastern arch separated.[23] After the defective work had been replaced, no further trouble was experienced. When the centerings blew down in a gale late in 1839, having in fact stood free of the structure since a year previously, the bridge remained standing and has done to this day.

Some miles beyond, between Twyford and Reading, a tunnel was originally proposed under Sonning Hill, but in the event the railway was driven through a 60 ft-deep cutting. Further west, the works were relatively light and the line, opened in stages, reached Hay Lane near Wootten Bassett by December 1840.

Meanwhile, construction had been proceeding from the Bristol end, under the supervision of the Bristol Committee. With their rather more lavish provision, Brunel was able to give free rein to his architectural powers on the works with which the short, 11½ mile, stretch of line to Bath fairly bristled. There were two viaducts, seven tunnels and a

Maidenhead bridge. Lithograph by J.C. Bourne, *The history and description of the Great Western Railway*, 1846.

Box tunnel. Lithograph in J.C. Bourne, *op. cit.*, 1846.

number of bridges. Many displayed Brunel's genius for elegant design and those in the region of Bath only add to its architectural splendours.

Brunel, his contractors and navvies pressed on to Chippenham and by May 1841, only the Chippenham to Bath section remained. It included the most difficult work on the whole line, the construction of Box tunnel. Nearly two miles long, it was 786 yards longer than Kilsby on the London & Birmingham, and the longest railway tunnel so far attempted. Another daring feature was that the line in the tunnel would be on a gradient of 1 in 100. The tunnel took five years to build, a year longer than planned. Apart from the ton of gunpowder a week used to blast out the Bath stone, the 247 000 cubic yards of material wrenched from under the hill was achieved by armies of navvies using pick and shovel, working by the light of candles. By the end of 1840, the work was seriously behind schedule and Brunel threw in all his forces, with 4000 men and 300 horses working day and night. The tunnel levied its toll in human lives – about 100 were lost in the course of the work. At last,

in June 1841 it was finished and the line could be opened throughout from London to Bristol, and even beyond, for the Bristol & Exeter Railway, incorporated in 1836, was completed as far as Bridgwater in the same month. On 30 June 1841, the inaugural train, bedecked with flags, conveyed the directors to Bristol in a shade over four hours, and on to Bridgwater in a further hour. They survived the 'monstrous and extraordinary, most dangerous and impracticable tunnel at Box'. At first, there was only a single track through the tunnel, and when there were two, the down line, going down the incline, was laid with a track specially designed by Brunel to restrict the speed of the trains. Speeding through the tunnel today in a brightly lit coach of a High Speed Train does not convey any idea of the experience of the first passengers, crawling along to take nearly twenty minutes in the tunnel, in total darkness in an unlit train. (The lighting of carriages, with oil lamps, was not introduced until the following year.) The line from London to Bridgwater was the longest in the world and was hailed as 'the most splendid monument to human genius and industry, in this or any country'[24]. The total cost of this great achievement is usually quoted as £6½ million, a rather handsome over-spend of the parliamentary estimate of £2½ million. But the total expended to 30 June 1841 is given in the company's printed reports and accounts as £5 877 120, and the first estimate to be given by Brunel after his initial survey was £2 805 330, or a mere 109% overspend. We must bear in mind that the railway engineers were at that time grappling with a form and scale of construction quite unprecedented. The overspend should be compared with that of the London & Birmingham Railway, opened in September 1838, and the line most nearly comparable in scale to the Great Western. Here, the estimate was £2½ million and the final bill £4 751 135, or 90% over.[25]

There were several reasons for the greater cost, of which the wider gauge was but one. It must be granted, first of all, that Brunel had achieved what he set out to achieve, to construct 'the finest work in England'. By laying out a route with beautifully level and even grading and gentle curves, he had provided a line highly conducive to smooth, fast and safe running, with benefits that are felt to this day by railway operators and travelling public alike, but particularly during the age of steam traction, as fast overall times could be achieved without the wear and tear of hard pulling up hills and hectic running down. But this route was not obtained without cost, as it entailed heavier earthworks that would have been avoided by a cheaper route following more nearly the lie of the land.

The broad gauge itself did contribute to the higher initial cost, although by no means in proportion.[26] It will be remembered that Brunel's original plan was for rolling stock of near normal width to lie within the wheels, so there was less need in laying out the track to provide for overhang on each side of the rails than there was on the standard gauge. The width of the land acquired to build the line from London to Bristol was very little greater than usual. Brunel had estimated the extra cost as only £50 a mile. During the proceedings of the Gauge Commission of 1845, the narrow gauge engineers made no mention of the land purchase factor, when they were concerned to make the most

Pangbourne station. Lithograph in J.C. Bourne, *op. cit.*, 1846.

Making a cutting on the Great Western Railway. Watercolour by George Childs, 1841, Science Museum.

of the disadvantages of the broad gauge, such as higher initial cost.

As to the works of construction, cross-sections of typical cuttings and embankments show little difference between the two systems. The width of the formation bed, that is, the ground on which was built up the ballast that actually supported the track, varied slightly from one standard gauge line to another. It tended to vary from about 25 ft to around the 29–30 ft recommended in such manuals of railway construction as R.M. Stephenson's of 1861.[27] The cuttings on the 37 narrow gauge lines that submitted information to the Commission varied from 26 ft to 33 ft, with an average of 30½ ft. The four broad gauge lines averaged 33 ft. On the Great Western itself, the figure was 30 ft, while the Bristol & Gloucester, constructed with tight clearances for broad gauge stock, had only 28 ft wide cuttings. On embankments, too, the difference was

negligible. Brunel's estimate of the cost increase on this account of about 6% is probably not far out. On some of the major single works such as viaducts, the difference was somewhat greater. Robert Stephenson estimated that with the higher viaducts such as the Wharncliffe, the added cost was nearly proportional to the increased width between parapets. Brunel states in his report to the directors of 13 July 1838 that their viaducts would be 30 ft wide, 2 ft more than on other lines, which he claimed raised the cost by only 6%. As the cost increase would have been in proportion to the widths, Brunel's estimate of 2½% was rather low.

The most expensive works, and those that exceeded their estimates by the greatest margin, on any railway, were the tunnels. However, in replying to Hawkshaw's estimates of the cost saving if the Great Western were to be standard gauge, after it had been constructed as far as Maidenhead, Brunel had claimed that the Box tunnel was to be made only 30 ft wide, only a few feet wider than standard gauge, and the same as was beginning to be recognised as the correct width. Stephenson's *Treatise* describes as standard a 30 ft wide tunnel, or 27 ft would do if the rock walls and base were hard enough to make a brick lining unnecessary. The drawings of Box and Twerton tunnels show a width of 30 ft, but that is inside the brick lining. It is therefore fair to reckon that a broad gauge tunnel was 3–4 ft wider than standard. With slight variations in practice on the standard gauge lines, there is no completely firm basis for comparing the broad gauge, and therefore a precise figure for the extra cost attributable strictly to this factor alone cannot be arrived at, but Brunel's estimate of about 8% given in his original report to the Board of September 1835 is probably about right.

Quite apart from the gauge, Brunel's design of track made it more expensive to construct, in time and materials. It is true that a particularly awkward, and as it turned out, unsatisfactory, feature, namely, the piling, was abandoned west of Maidenhead. But another difficulty arose. The bridge rails specified by Brunel had less vertical stiffness than a rail of the same weight but of solid section, in the proportion, so it was reckoned, of 5 to 7. The consequence was that a locomotive tended to crush down the rail as it passed over it, and the rail cut into the longitudinal timber bearing. So 10 ft lengths of hardwood, ¾ inch thick 'pine packing', as it came to be called, had to be nailed to the bearings. A layer of felt was inserted to deaden the noise of running.[28] All this made it more expensive to lay than the stone block or cross-sleeper systems used on other lines. The wider gauge added little or nothing to the work of laying the track, and only about 5 % to the materials, mostly timber.

One further reason for added expense has to be noted, and that is the personality and hence the method of working of the Engineer himself – Brunel. F.R. Conder,[29] a railway engineer, worked on a number of the leading railways during their periods of construction and later on compiled his reminiscences, which provide a fascinating insight into the working methods of such giants of railway engineering as Brunel and Robert Stephenson. Conder remarked that Brunel's method of administration resembled 'that of the Spanish monarchy rather than that of a constitutional government'. Stephenson delegated authority to competent assistants who superintended the detailed work, although he was well aware of what was going on 'on the ground'. Brunel, on the other hand, while retaining a vision of his grand design, took a close, personal interest in the most minute details. This near-obsession with detail and inability to leave it to subordinates goes far to explain the punishing work programme Brunel inflicted on himself during the construction of the Great Western. This trait several times irritated Daniel Gooch, Brunel's highly competent engineer in charge of locomotives and rolling stock, who found his 'Chief' fussing over matters that lay well within his own competence. But Brunel tended to gather round him assistants of more questionable ability and the effect on those was to make them even more pernickety than their Chief lest they risk a rebuke for failing to maintain standards. And Brunel's standards for quality in materials and workmanship were unrelentingly high. Contractors in the early stages were finding to their dismay that work had

to be undone and repeated at unpleasant expense, whereas it would have passed muster on other undertakings. The inevitable result was that, forewarned and as an insurance against this kind of mishap, contractors would, if they could be persuaded to tender at all, estimate high, and the company had to pay dearly for work that elsewhere would have cost much less.

Although the cost had undeniably been heavy, there was no doubt about the quality of the result, which provided the locomotives built to Gooch's designs ample opportunity to show their paces. It was the 'Firefly' class, of the 2–2–2 type with 7 ft driving wheels that more than any established the Great Western's early reputation for speed and economy. On the opening day of the entire line, the inaugural train reached Bristol in two minutes over four hours, or half an hour quicker than Brunel had undertaken to achieve. That was thought to be the only time on record that an engineer had exceeded his promises, 'and highly adds to the honour of Mr. Brunel'[24].

In 1844, the Bristol & Exeter Railway was completed and Gooch drove the first train from London to Exeter and back, coming up in 4 hr 40 min., with a locomotive of the 'Firefly' class. This was a notable achievement, not least by Gooch himself, who had a very long day of it. 'Next day my

Firefly locomotive. Science Museum scale drawing.

Royal Albert Bridge, Saltash. Lithograph, Science Museum.

back ached so I would hardly walk'. Better was to come, for when the new track settled down, the schedule of the fastest train was, in May 1845, cut to 4 hr 30 m. for the 194 miles, or an average speed including stops of 43.9 mph. These trains were the fastest anywhere, and were really the world's first express trains.

The broad gauge Bristol & Exeter Railway had been incorporated in 1836 and leased to the Great Western in 1840. The lease expired nine years later and the line led an independent existence until it was finally taken over by the Great Western in 1876. The parent company was, of course, anxious to carve out for itself a broad gauge empire in the west of England, and so it looked beyond Exeter. The South Devon Railway from Exeter to Plymouth was authorised in July 1844 and launched with capital subscribed by the Great Western, Bristol & Exeter and Bristol & Gloucester Companies. Brunel again was appointed engineer but reasons of economy prevented him from following an easily

graded route with heavy earthworks, and the route took a level course as far as Newton Abbot, but then went up hill and down dale towards Plymouth, with the steepest gradients to be found on a British main line. Plymouth was reached in 1849 and the Cornwall and West Cornwall Railways took the line westwards to Penzance, completion only being achieved with the opening in 1859 of the last and greatest of Brunel's railway works, the Royal Albert Bridge over the River Tamar.

With various branches, the broad gauge line from London to Penzance conformed to Brunel's conception of a broad gauge enclave sealed off from other lines. But the noble conception began to crack when the Great Western turned northwards into the West Midlands, while the northern lines looked south.

The Cheltenham & Great Western Union Railway was completed in 1845, linking Cheltenham and Gloucester with the main line, at a junction near the small town of Swindon. It was here that it was decided to set up the main works for the repair of locomotives, and from 1846 the construction of new locomotives. That same year, the South Wales Railway was incorporated, giving access to London by way of Gloucester. Meanwhile, a route was being developed having momentous consequences for the gauge question, that between Bristol and Birmingham. Both cities had strong interests in a direct rail link and both the Great Western, from the Bristol end, and the Midland Railway, from Birmingham, recognised this. The Birmingham & Gloucester Company completed their line to standard gauge in 1840. To the south, the Bristol & Gloucester Company, with origins in coal tramroads north of Bristol, projected a route from Bristol to Standish, on the broad gauge Cheltenham & Great Western Union, 7½ miles short of Gloucester. With broad gauge at each end, they were persuaded to construct the whole line to this gauge, completing it in 1844. The company then joined forces with the Birmingham & Gloucester and a new Bristol & Birmingham Company opened negotiations with the Great Western. If these had succeeded, the Birmingham & Gloucester would have fallen under Great Western influence

and doubtless have been converted to 7 ft gauge. But while the Great Western were driving a hard bargain, the Midland snapped up the Bristol & Birmingham from under the nose of the Great Western. So from Birmingham the traveller bound for Bristol set out in a narrow gauge train and at Gloucester, about half way, had to change to a broad gauge one for the rest of the way. A railway map of 1845 marks ten 'breaks-of-gauge', but none was to achieve such notoriety as Gloucester. The impediment to passengers and goods traffic was real and considerable, as it was bound to be on such a vital route, but the narrow gauge interest magnified it still further. The 'Battle of the Gauges' was on and Gloucester was the front line.

Meanwhile, the Great Western were promoting two lines that passed north from the terminus of their Oxford branch, opened on 12 June 1844, the Oxford, Worcester & Wolverhampton and the Oxford & Rugby lines. These threatened to carry the broad gauge right into narrow gauge territory and not surprisingly incurred vigorous opposition from the companies to the north. During the committee

The break of gauge at Gloucester. Engraving in *Illustrated London News*, 1845, 6 June, p. 369.

stage on the bills for the two lines, the arguments for and against the two gauges raged back and forth.[30] This time, the Great Western and the broad gauge won the day, although, if required by the Board of Trade, a third rail would have to be laid on the Oxford & Rugby and parts of the OW&W to enable narrow gauge trains to run – mixed gauge. The two bills were passed by both Houses and received the Royal Assent on 4 August 1845. By that time, however, on Richard Cobden's initiative, a Royal Commission had been appointed to consider the possibility of insisting on a uniform gauge in the future. One member was Colonel Sir Frederick Smith, who had been the first Inspector–General of Railways to the Board of Trade and was the one who inspected and approved the Great Western before its opening in 1841. The second was Peter Barlow, Professor of Mathematics at the Royal Military Academy at Woolwich; he had been associated with the Irish Railway Commission in 1836 and subsequent railway matters and, as *The Times* remarked, he knew more about railways than any other person who was not practically engaged in them. Finally, Lieutenant Harness was invited to serve but declined, whereupon the invitation was extended to George Biddell Airy, Astronomer–Royal.[31] There is no reason to suppose a fairer-minded or more knowledgeable body could have been assembled, bearing in mind that all those 'practically engaged' in railways were excluded on account of their strong interest in the victory of one gauge or the other. The printed record of the evidence given over the months from August to December 1845 shows that the examination of the 48 witnesses was for the most part fair and shrewd.[32]

They were charged with considering whether future Acts of Parliament authorising the construction of railways should insist on uniformity of gauge, whether it was expedient and practicable to bring all existing lines into a uniform gauge, and whether there were any means of mitigating the evils of breaks of gauge. The Commissioners set about their task chiefly by interviewing witnesses, who included the leading railway engineers of the day, such as Brunel, Robert Stephenson, Joseph Locke and Daniel Gooch; they included the leading promoters of railways and those engaged in administering them, such as George Hudson, Mark Huish, C.A. Saunders of the Great Western and John Ellis, then deputy chairman of the Midland. Not overlooked were representatives of carriers such as Pickfords who had first hand experience of sending goods through Gloucester, nor were Her Majesty's Inspectors of Railways. Finally, senior army officers gave their opinion on the likely effect of a break of gauge on troop movements in an emergency.

Daniel Gooch in 1845, aged 29, with a model of a 'Firefly' class locomotive. Science Museum photograph.

The unrehearsed replies of witnesses with varied and first hand experience of railway operation provide a real insight into British railway practice in the mid–1840s, together with the financial and technical data of 41 railway companies, that make up the 852 folio pages of the printed Report and Minutes of Evidence of the Gauge Commission. When pressed for detailed information, many of the witnesses promised to obtain it for the Commissioners. Brunel, in particular, explained that he had only just returned home and did not have his notes with him; he was in fact heavily engaged in marine engineering at the time. Gooch on the other hand was a shining exception, armed with masses of technical data, and the printed record of his evidence is fairly peppered with the phrase *The witness produced a table.* The examination of the witnesses was supplemented by observations of various aspects of railway practice, including the proceedings at Gloucester, and culminated in the trials of broad and narrow gauge locomotive performance, carried out at Brunel's suggestion.

The report first considered the effects of the break of gauge at Gloucester, that being the only one then in existence, on express trains, ordinary or mixed trains, goods trains and on 'the conveyance of Your Majesty's forces'. The effects were increasingly serious in the first three categories, while in the fourth, the country could be exposed to serious danger. The average delay to passengers, according to the guards' journals for August 1845, was only 16 minutes, which, as Gooch pointed out, could easily be exceeded at Birmingham, changing from one line to another. Goods, however, were a differernt matter. As the railway network developed and through routes from one company to another were set up, first the possibilities and then the necessity for through goods traffic were realised. The financial complexities of through booking were completely resolved by the setting up of the admirable Railway Clearing House in 1842. The physical obstructions were minimal – except at Gloucester. The scenes of appalling chaos that were caricatured and, in one case anyway, were deliberately engineered for the benefit of a visiting parliamentary committee, were an exaggeration. But the expense and inconvenience were real enough. The

average delay of goods trains was 4½ to 5½ hours, during which the army of porters that had to be permanently on hand, and paid for, manhandled the goods, whether separate articles, minerals such as coal, or livestock, from the wagons of one gauge to the other, with consequent risk of loss or damage. The company had the added expense of maintaining virtually twice as many wagons to cope with the traffic as if it were worked through from Birmingham to Bristol. Gloucester was bad enough, but the evil would spread; the Commissioners were gravely concerned about the effect on the projected important through north–south route of which the Oxford to Rugby Railway would be a vital link.

Various devices could have been installed at Gloucester to make it unnecessary to tranship the goods. A crane had actually been erected there but it seems never to have been used. Brunel's sketch books reveal an ingenious method of hoisting a container from the undercarriage of one wagon to another, but it was never constructed. The broad gauge advocates were curiously backward in developing such devices. They could then have countered the arguments of one witness after another when the Commissioners pressed for their views on the practicability and safety of the various methods available. Telescopic axles, expanding to the 7 ft gauge, were quickly discounted. Broad gauge trucks with narrow gauge rails on them on which the narrow wagons could run, were ruled out as broad gauge bridges were scarcely higher than the others, so there was insufficient headroom for the combined vehicle. Lifting the body of a wagon from one undercarriage to another had its drawbacks as the undercarriage derived much of its strength from the superstructure and it would have added to the expense and the weight to make it strong enough. Finally, the loose-box, or in modern terms 'container', idea was considered, but felt to be unsafe and also unsuited to the miscellaneous nature of the goods that were trundled around the country. The Commission therefore concluded that there were no means of reducing significantly the inconvenience at a break of gauge. That led them to decide that a uniform gauge was an overriding need. But which one? They considered the question from the aspects of safety, accommodation

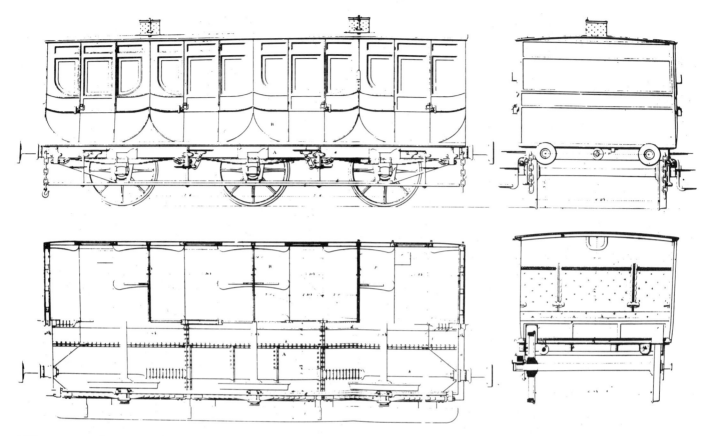

GW 1st class carriage, 1840s. Courtesy of British Rail, Western Region.

and convenience of passengers and goods, speed and economy.

As to safety, there had been a vague feeling that a broader base would lead to greater stability and therefore safety. But five years of Accident Reports of the Railways Inspecting Officers had shown little difference in the safety of the two systems. McConnell, at that time locomotive superintendent on the Bristol & Birmingham, saw no difference between the two gauges of which he had the oversight. Safe running depended on several factors, above all the quality of the track, but the gauge had little to do with it. Gooch maintained that the Great Western 'baulk road' was safer, for a vehicle could be derailed at speed and the wheels run along the timber bearing until the train came to a halt, whereas on transverse sleepers a serious smash would have occurred. Indeed, he knew of a case where the van marshalled between the engine and carriages was derailed before Reading, ran along the timber and then re-railed itself some miles further on without the driver or the passengers being any the wiser. But that was a tribute to the baulk road, not the 7 ft gauge.

On the second point, the accommodation and convenience of passengers and goods, the Commissioners found little preference for either. With hindsight, this seems a curious conclusion, but they, like everyone else, saw railways as they were or were likely to be in the near

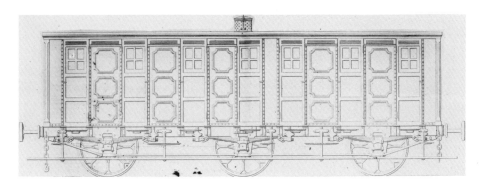

GW 3rd class carriage, 1840s. Courtesy of British Rail, Western Region.

future. Brunel's lone predictions of bigger (broad gauge) trains at higher speeds were not taken seriously. Great Western compartments were certainly roomier – 9 ft wide compared to 7 ft 6 in., and 6 ft high, so one could stand upright. Bruyere of the London & Birmingham proudly claimed that their latest carriages enabled him to sit down with his hat on and still have 4 inches to spare. It was generally agreed that three first class passengers a side on the narrow gauge had at least as much room as the four a side on the Great Western, and with a greater proportion enjoying the coveted corner seats. But the Great Western went one better, and for its new express trains introduced first class carriages that for spaciousness and comfort were only exceeded by Royal saloons. Samuel Sidney, a noted railway writer on the narrow gauge side, made the carping criticism that the Great Western were catering only for the rich, for the Member of Parliament who wished to be sped in comfort to his West Country constituency, while condemning the majority, in the second or third class, to gruelling hardship. The latest Great Western 2nd class carriages could seat as many as 72 passengers, but in the days when railways added a coach to a train to avoid overcrowding, a 72-seater would increase the weight of the train unnecessarily if there were only a handful of passengers to be accommodated. Conditions in the 2nd class provoked letters of stormy abuse in *The Times*, but the plight of the 3rd class passenger found no similar outlet. Their conditions were bad enough for the Government to intervene, with Gladstone's Railway Act of 1844. This enacted, among other things, that 3rd class passengers had

to be given seating and adequate protection from the weather and at least one train a day calling at all stations and averaging not less than 12 mph. Like some other companies, the Great Western stayed within the law, just. One train a day, with 3rd class coaches and goods vehicles, took about 9 hours to travel 118 miles from Paddington to Bristol. Even so, they were still better off than they had been on the roads.

The comfort of the journey depended very much then, as now, on the condition of the track, and that could be very variable on all lines. Transverse wooden sleepers had largely superseded stone blocks and gave a much smoother ride, but the fishplate joint, or metal plate bolted to the ends of the rails to hold them together, was still a few years away. (It was patented in 1847.) The Great Western bridge rail firmly secured to the continuous bearing was better in this respect. Carriage size and design also had an effect. The Commissioners heard conflicting evidence, and concluded that one could experience smooth and rough riding on both systems, but that on the broad gauge travel was 'generally more easy at high velocities'.

For goods, the broad gauge seemed at the time less suited to the miscellaneous small loads that formed much of the traffic. The Great Western wagons were larger and heavier but, loaded, their overall width was little greater than the narrow gauge, the latter having a greater overhang. Harding, a fierce protagonist of the narrow gauge, asserted that on the Bristol and Birmingham 219 tons of goods conveyed in 48 broad gauge wagons weighing 228 tons unloaded were transferred to 65 narrow gauge wagons only

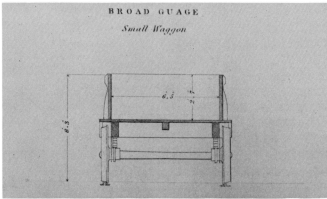

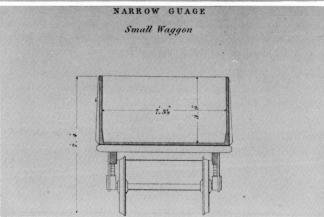

Broad and narrow gauge wagons compared. Engraving in *Observations on the Report of the Gauge Commissioners*, 1846.

169 tons tare. Thus, as with the carriages, there was greater dead weight to be carried on the Great Western, no mean consideration with locomotives of limited haulage capacity.

In the matter of speed, the advantage lay clearly with the broad gauge. Its new fast train, reaching Exeter in 4 hours 25 minutes from Paddington, set a standard unparalleled anywhere in the world. Before that, its best trains were faster, spurring the narrow gauge on to try and catch up. The Exeter express had, as we have seen, the great benefit of Brunel's magnificently laid-out route and a track that was rather more conducive at the time to high speed running. But the speed was achieved by the locomotives designed by

Daniel Gooch. Most railways simply ordered one of the few basic designs that were available from the main locomotive manufacturers, including the Stephenson 'Patentee' design originating in 1833. Gooch however was one of the first locomotive superintendents to make his own designs. He based them on the only two locomotives he could rely on in the early days, the *North Star* and *Morning Star*, which were themselves of the 'Patentee' type, that is with inside cylinders between sandwich frames carried on 6 wheels, the middle pair being the driving wheels. The result, essentially an enlargement of the 'Stars', was the famous 'Firefly' class, delivered in 1840–2. At that time it was firmly believed, mistakenly as it turned out, that a high centre of gravity would make a locomotive unstable in running and unsafe, and the need to keep it low determined a number of design features. With a much broader base, Gooch felt justified in pitching the boiler higher, over the axle of 7 ft diameter driving wheels; that was felt to be conducive to higher speeds and without excessively raising piston speeds. Then, Gooch employed a boiler of greater diameter, that could 'sit down' between the cranks and valve gear, whereas on a narrow-gauge engine the boiler would have to be raised to clear them, and that was ruled out by the centre of gravity fetish. In addition the wider gauge enabled Gooch to fit wider driving wheel bearings and with these the Great Western locomotives could run 60–70000 miles before lifting and examining the brasses, compared with 20–30000 for narrow gauge. It was admitted that narrow gauge locomotive engineers had difficulty in 'crowding in' the mechanism and bearings between the frames.

It was generally recognised that a boiler of adequate capacity to produce steam was essential and in particular, as Gooch put it, 'the firebox is really the test of the power of the engine'. Here the 7 ft gauge was a real advantage, for Gooch put in the *Firefly* a firebox 4 ft 9 in. wide, 6 inches wider than could be accommodated in the rival gauge.

On the narrow gauge, the boiler had to be lengthened to increase its capacity; the result was Stephenson's 'long boiler' locomotive. Its 12 ft long copper tubes were thought to be more liable to sag than the 10 ft tubes of *Firefly*. Also, to provide adequate draught for the fire, a sharper blast was

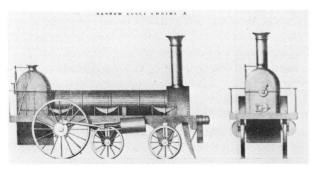

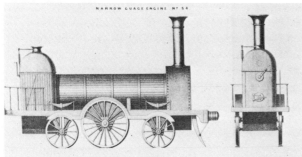

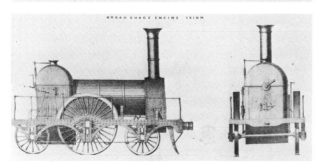

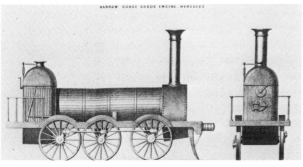

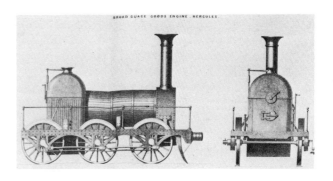

Locomotives that took part in the Gauge Commission trials.
Engraving in *Supplemental observations on the published evidence
. . . of the Gauge Commissioners*, 1846.

required – 8–9 inches of vacuum in the smokebox, Gooch
calculated, compared to 5–6 inches. That produced greater
back pressure in the cylinders, greater wear in the tubes and
tubes choked with ash. As if that was not enough, the
wheelbase of the 'long boiler' was crowded between
smokebox and firebox, with a large overhang fore and aft,
making a locomotive alarmingly unstable at high speed.

Gooch said of one of these locomotives, known as the
Great A, completed by Stephenson just in time to take part
in the locomotive trials conducted for the Commissioners, 'I
found the engine exceedingly unsteady, so much so that I
doubted the safety of it, and deterred Mr. Brunel from
returning upon it'.

Brunel had suggested the trials to enable the narrow
gauge party to make good their claim that their locomotives
could match those of the Great Western in performance and
efficiency. The *Great A* showed its paces on the 44 almost
level miles between York and Darlington, while Gooch's
Ixion of the 'Firefly' class performed over the 53-mile
stretch from Paddington to Didcot. Precise details of the
times, speeds, loads hauled and consumption of water and
coke are recorded with the *Commission Report*. *Ixion*
outshone *Great A*. For example, on its first day, 16

December 1845, *Ixion* hauled 8 10-ton carriages up the faintly rising grades towards Didcot, averaging 52.8 mph between the 4th and 50th mileposts; coming back, the average was 55.23 mph; top speeds were 55 and 58. With the same load, *Great A* averaged 45.4 mph between the 4th and 42nd mileposts, up slightly less favourable grades, with a maximum of 51. *Ixion* had consumed 33.6lbs of coke a mile, *Great A* 26.6. Honours rested with the broad gauge, but the narrow gauge performance was quite respectable.

On the final point of comparison, that of economy, a welter of data were submitted, in which the Commissioners had to pick their way carefully. It was clear that the initial cost of the broad gauge was greater, but, as we have seen, not nearly in proportion to the increase in gauge. But it was difficult to make a precise, quantitative, comparison as Brunel's track system was different; the track itself was originally expected to be cheaper, but as timbers and rails heavier than those originally proposed had to be used, it proved to be more expensive to lay. In maintenance, records from the engineer's office at Oxford show the broad gauge baulk road cost £165 16s 4d a mile, compared to the narrow gauge £176 1s 1d. But we are again not comparing like with like; broad gauge track on transverse sleepers would have required 50% more timber and ballast to renew.

The Great Western locomotives and rolling stock were more expensive to construct. Gooch's locomotives cost around £1850 each; Bury's small four-wheel engines for the London & Birmingham were only about £1250, and the latest long-boiler *White Horse of Kent* for the Southampton line was £1700. Against that, Gooch quoted lighter repair costs for the Great Western, at 2.7d per mile, compared with 3.46d on the narrow gauge. The average total locomotive cost per mile of four narrow gauge railways was £204 13s 1d and for the Great Western £179 19s 8d. The narrow gauge figure was raised notably by the London & Birmingham's need to use two of its small Bury locomotives per train, whereas a *Firefly* could handle Great Western trains singlehanded.

The data flew back and forth and the Commissioners were faced with a mass of conflicting evidence. One fact stood out with stark clarity: 1901 miles of 4ft 8½in. railway had been completed by July 1845 but only 274 miles of 7ft. It was also clear that gauge uniformity was already a necessity, and it was hardly feasible to widen the narrow gauge; the tunnels alone virtually ruled that out. Their conclusion was therefore inescapable: they recommended that 4ft 8½in. should be declared by Parliament as the gauge for all railways under construction or to be constructed; that the gauge of no line should be altered without Parliament's consent; that the north–south narrow gauge link should be completed by joining the proposed Oxford to Rugby line with a narrow gauge line from Oxford to Reading and Basingstoke, or any shorter link with the London & South Western; and that to achieve uniformity and avoid the evils of breaks of gauge, an equitable means of converting the broad gauge track should be found, or of enabling narrow gauge trains to pass safely over broad gauge metals.

Far from settling the controversy, hostilities broke out afresh with a war of pamphlets,[33] ranging from the reasoned to the scurrilous. Brunel and Saunders challenged the findings[34] and a torrent of anti-broad gauge propaganda was let loose from the other side, but added little to a serious consideration of the issue. The Great Western riposte may however have had an effect on the Government, for when *An Act for regulating the Gauge of Railways*[35] received the Royal Assent on 18 August 1846, the Great Western were let off more lightly than they might have expected. True, it was enacted that the gauge of all future railways in Great Britain should be 4ft 8½in., or 5ft 3in. in Ireland, unless any present or future act contained a 'special enactment defining the gauge'. Certain lines, such as those in Cornwall, Devon, Dorset and Somerset were exempted, while for certain other lines, including the South Wales line, 7ft was actually specified. The Oxford, Worcester & Wolverhampton, and the Oxford & Rugby lines were allowed to go ahead unaffected by the Act. It seemed like business as usual for the Great Western, for the broad gauge could not only continue in existence but carry on its development programme. We have seen how the route to the west progressed; with the completion of the bridge over the Tamar, the broad gauge reached Truro in 1859. The

Baker Street station on the Metropolitan Railway, 1863. Lithograph, Science Museum.

West Cornwall Railway on to Penzance, originally constructed to narrow gauge, was 'mixed' in the mid-1860s and eventually the first broad gauge passenger train ran through from Paddington to Penzance on 1 March 1867.

To the south, the principal line was to Weymouth, opened in 1857, with mixed gauge over the final length from Dorchester, shared with the London & South Western. Further north, the South Wales Railway, with Brunel as engineer, was laid as a double track broad gauge line, from Grange Court on the Cheltenham to Swindon line, through Newport and Swansea to New Milford, later Neyland, reached in 1856. (The extension to Fishguard came much later.) Feeding this main route from the mining valleys of South Wales were a number of branches on narrow gauge. Brunel had indeed recommended this gauge for the Taff Vale Railway, as being more suitable for sharply curved track. Brunel was not bigoted on the matter of gauge; it should be chosen to suit the conditions. This admirable attitude brought severe problems in South Wales, to which, as we shall see, there was only one solution.

Further north lay disputed territory. In its drive northwards from Oxford to Rugby and north west to Wolverhampton and on towards the Mersey, the Great Western was faced by the London & North Western Railway, formed in 1846 by amalgamation of principally the London & Birmingham and Grand Junction. The broad gauge pressed north to Banbury and later on to Birmingham, but the line to Rugby from a junction at Fenny Compton, beyond Banbury, was never built, owing to the hostility of the LNW. To serve the west midlands, the Oxford, Worcester & Wolverhampton Railway was incorporated in 1845 and intended to form part of the broad gauge empire, although mixed gauge was to be provided to enable junctions to be made with the Birmingham & Bristol and LNW, at Wolverhampton. It is not necessary here to describe once more the endless difficulties into which it plunged the Great Western. Suffice it to say that it richly deserved its nickname 'Old Worse and Worse'. In spite of the original provision, it first laid only narrow gauge track, with a token length of mixed gauge laid on the down line of the northern part, with no crossings or sidings. Repeated efforts by the Great Western to have mixed gauge laid for the entire line were of no avail, for a 37-mile portion of the up line beyond Evesham obstinately remained pure narrow gauge.

Broad or mixed gauge construction continued spasmodically through the 1860s and 70s. The first portion of the London underground was opened on mixed gauge in 1863 from Paddington to Farringdon Street, and finally in the far west the branch from St. Erth to St. Ives was constructed to broad gauge as late as 1877. But by then the mileage had begun to shrink.

After the gauge war, the Great Western was finding it increasingly difficult to regard itself as a self-contained

Conversion to narrow gauge at
Teignmouth, 1892. Courtesy of British
Rail, Western Region.

broad gauge enclave, or to maintain transhipment points
where it met the narrow gauge without serious loss of traffic
and revenue. It had to accept the expedient of mixed gauge,
by which a third rail was laid within the 7 ft track, the outer
rail being common to both gauges. It was an expensive
arrangement, costing about £2300 a mile of double line. Not
only that, mixed gauge was far more expensive to maintain,
at £251 18s 5d a mile, compared to the £165–£176 for single
gauge quoted by A.W. Gooch at Oxford.[36] On the open
road, laying the third rail was simple enough but at
junctions and stations the pointwork for mixed gauge
became incredibly complicated. Although the general
impression given to the Gauge Commission was that this
would be a safety hazard, these fears seem to have been
groundless, for the GW maintained a good safety record.
But there was a further complication. Turntables were often
used to transfer wagons from one track to another, and they
had to stand centrally or the turntable would have been out
of balance. So a fourth rail had to be laid in the approach
track and on the turntable to place narrow gauge wagons

centrally within the 7 ft rails. The third rail appeared on
various parts of the system, but the year 1861 brought
narrow gauge trains into Paddington itself. The Oxford,
Worcester & Wolverhampton had turned out as a narrow
gauge railway and the only way to enable trains to run
through to London was to lay the rail from Oxford through
Didcot and Reading to Paddington. Eventually mixed
gauge had penetrated as far west as Exeter.

By the end of 1866, the broad gauge reached its highest
mileage, of lines open or under construction, of 1040, with
an additional 387 miles of mixed gauge. Of this the Great
Western owned or worked 592 miles of broad and 240 of
mixed gauge, with a further 462 of narrow gauge. There
were about 30 places where the broad met the narrow gauge
and there was increasing pressure from commerce for the
GW to rid itself of this evil.[37] In spite of the stay of
execution granted by the Gauge Act, it must have been clear
that the broad gauge was doomed and when the traders of
South Wales made a firm request to the Board for the
conversion of the main line there to narrow gauge, the end

must have seemed in sight. But conversion was an intricate and expensive task and the Company's finances were, in common with some others at that time, at a low ebb. Gooch, having resigned as locomotive superintendent in 1864, had been persuaded to return as Chairman two years later, to guide the Company through a period of careful austerity. He aimed to 'cut down all capital expenditure to a minimum'. This was not a good time to ask for major track conversion, but by 1869 the Company declared a dividend of 3¾%, the highest for 18 years. It is surely not a coincidence that conversions began about this time. The first sizeable length to be narrowed lay between Hereford and Grange Court, near Gloucester, a distance of 22½ miles. The work was completed in 8 days from 16 August 1869. This provided valuable experience for a really large-scale exercise, the conversion of the South Wales Railway, 188 miles of double track and 48 of single, in April and May of 1872. The last broad gauge train ran on 11 May, collecting broad gauge vehicles as it lumbered east, hauled by a 2–4–0 locomotive named *Brunel*. In May also, the Swindon–Cheltenham line was narrowed, so that by this

time the mileage of broad gauge track had been roughly halved. The cost was £402 000, £226 000 for permanent way and civil engineering work, the rest for the new narrow gauge rolling stock acquired to work the lines. Two years later attention was turned south of the main line and the line to Weymouth, with the Salisbury branch, was narrowed. To carry out these operations with as little dislocation to the service as possible required the most careful preparation, meticulous planning and great discipline and devotion among the workforce. The 110 route miles of the 1874 conversion required the services of 1800 men, organised into gangs of 20 for each mile or so. There was a hierarchy of about 100 gangers-in-charge, 20 inspectors and 5 or 6 assistants to the chief engineer. Each gang was issued with a supply of sugar and oatmeal, which a member of the gang was deputed to boil up into a GW drink known as 'skilly'. It was found to be more thirst-quenching than other beverages. Smoking and alcohol were forbidden.

Conversion of mixed gauge was a simple matter of collecting up the broad gauge stock and then removing one rail. On unmixed track on transverse sleepers, additional

Conversion to narrow gauge at Plymouth, Millbay, 1892. Courtesy of British Rail, Western Region.

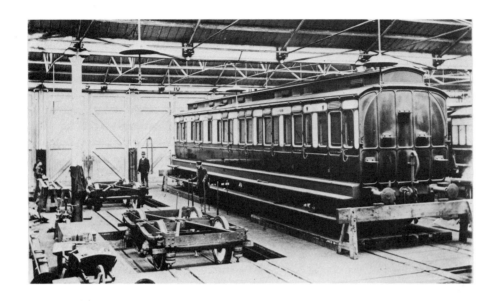

Equipment for changing broad to narrow gauge bogies. Photograph by Rev. A.H. Malan, Public Record Office.

chairs were fixed at the correct position and one rail was then lifted from the outer to the inner chairs. The baulk road was different: the transoms, or cross-members at 11 ft intervals were marked, partially and then on conversion day completely sawn through and one longitudinal bearing with its rail was moved bodily in to its new position.

Graphic descriptions of day-to-day life in a conversion team are given by several authors, for which the reader is referred to the *Notes and References*.[38] Less attention has been paid to the problems of the locomotive and carriage departments at Swindon. Their heavy load of work in breaking up broad gauge stock and providing for the standard gauge was a factor in determining the timing of the conversions. 'Convertible' stock eased the problem somewhat. Standard carriages were constructed with temporary 7 ft bogies, which could easily be replaced with standard gauge ones. Substituting these bogies was reduced to a fine art; on one occasion a party of special visitors took train, broad gauge, from South Wales to Swindon. The changeover was completed while they were refreshing themselves in the station restaurant, and they returned home narrow gauge. In the years before the final extinction in 1892, convertible locomotives were built, with the wheels

outside the double frames; they were to reappear as narrow gauge machines with the wheels between the frames. There were at the last only 196 broad gauge locomotives of which 127 were convertibles[38a].

After the spate of track conversions in the 1870s, the GW had by 1876 no purely broad gauge lines left, for all its track mileage was narrow or mixed gauge. This situation did not last long for in the same year, the Bristol & Exeter and railways to the west were at last amalgamated with the GW. This included the 106-mile stretch of unmixed 7 ft line from Exeter to Truro, with branches in addition. (The route on to Penzance of the old West Cornwall Railway had been laid down to narrow gauge and so at the amalgamation was mixed.) For the next 16 years the broad gauge lingered on, the Paddington to Penzance trains being the only broad gauge expresses left. They looked and ran much as they had for the last 40 years and more, for the realisation that it was doomed laid a dead hand on its technology, and design and practice were virtually stagnant during that time. It was indeed fortunate that Brunel and Gooch had placed it so far in advance of its time, back in the 1840s. Gooch mentioned to the Gauge Commissioners in October 1845 that an enlarged version of the 'Firefly' class was contemplated.

The order was not placed until the turn of the year, while the latest long boiler engine was showing its paces north of York, for it is known that design and construction took a mere 13 weeks, and the engine, the *Great Western* steamed from Swindon works on 1 April 1846, the first locomotive to be completely constructed there. It was carried on the same 2–2–2 chassis as the 'Fireflies' but it had a much larger boiler, with high haystack firebox and larger cylinders (18 in × 24 in) and driving wheels no less than 8 ft in diameter. This magnificent machine was soon breaking records, with a round trip to Exeter in 208 minutes down and 211 minutes up, running times, for the 194 miles. The front axle carried an undue proportion of the weight and it broke; two axles were substituted, giving a wheel arrangement usually quoted as 4–2–2, but more correctly 2–2–2–2, as the front four carrying wheels were not set in a bogie frame. The following year, a fleet of similar locomotives began to appear, the principal modification being that a round-topped firebox replaced the haystack pattern. The class took its name from the first example: *Iron Duke*. During the initial building period, 1847 to 1855, 29 were built. Their dimensions, widely quoted in railway literature, are summarised in the *Notes and references*.[39] They weighed 35½ tons, 12.3 tons on the driving axle, the heaviest engines of the time and in performance they excelled too. They immediately made possible an acceleration of the Exeter express to 2½ hours to Bristol and 4 hours 25 minutes to Exeter. It was scheduled to reach its first stop at Didcot, 53 miles, in 55 minutes. The load was usually six 8-ton carriages, conveying both 1st and 2nd class passengers and a van, or including the tender, passengers and luggage, nearly 80 tons. This performance put the Great Western far ahead of other lines, in this country or anywhere. It is true that the narrow gauge party showed they too could achieve a 35-ton locomotive, the *Liverpool*, designed by Thomas Crampton. Its pair of driving wheels were placed at the rear, behind the boiler and firebox, which could therefore be kept low – centre of

gravity again. It performed well, averaging 50 mph with a 150-ton train.[40] But the London & North Western track did not take as kindly to such a locomotive as Brunel's baulk road and this flirtation with big Crampton engines was nipped in the bud. It should however be mentioned that similar locomotives gave good service on the South Eastern Railway and were popular on several railways on the Continent. But here, the 'Iron Dukes' reigned supreme and handled the broad gauge trains as far as Exeter, later Newton Abbot, until the end in 1892. From 1870 they began to show signs of wear and were gradually withdrawn from service, to be replaced by new locomotives with only minor modifications such as the raising of the boiler pressure from 100 to 140 lb/in^2. Of these, 24 were built in batches from 1871 to 1888, nearly all perpetuating the names of the earlier locomotives, such as *Great Western* and *Iron Duke*.

E.L. Ahrons,[41] noted authority on railway matters of the late 19th and early 20th century, has left us his impressions of latter-day broad gauge working. The schedules of the best expresses were actually a little slower than they had been when the 'Iron Dukes' were new; 87 minutes were allowed for the 77¼ miles to Swindon, but Ahrons said that speed rarely attained 60 mph and a few minutes were

8-foot single locomotive *Lightning* at Newton Abbot in July 1889. Photograph by Rev. A.H. Malan, Public Record Office.

Down mail train passing Uphill Junction between Bristol and Taunton hauled by *Inkerman*, in the 1880s. Photograph by Rev. A.H. Malan, Public Record Office.

usually lost. They could easily be regained on the leisurely timing of the downhill run on to Bath, 37 minutes for 29½ miles. Further west, the performance was rather more lively; the schedule of the up 'Zulu', 11.15 am from Penzance, was only 38 minutes for the 30.8 miles from Exeter to Taunton, rising over Whiteball summit, a time that was still standard in the later days of steam. It was with this train that Ahrons noted the highest speed he had ever experienced. The driver of the *Lightning*, with Ahrons on the footplate, touched 81 mph or thereabouts down Wellington bank. This appears to have been a special effort, although the 8-footers regularly exceeded 70 at this point.

Greater demands were in fact being made on the locomotives as loads had increased. In 1874, the six-wheeled carriages used for so long on the broad gauge trains at last began to give way to the eight-wheeled vehicles designed by Dean. At 24 or 25 tons apiece, a train of 5 or 6 of them exceeded the 65–70 tons of the earlier trains. Some were built to the full width possible on the 7 ft gauge, 10 ft 6 in.

Seating four first class passengers a side, on luxurious upholstery, travel was very comfortable indeed. Second class passengers were rather less generously treated but still enjoyed the privilege of broad gauge express travel, a privilege denied to the third class passenger, who travelled in more austere conditions, although the 7 a side were not more cramped than 6 a side in later narrow gauge commuter carriages. For local trains and branch lines, the six-wheelers soldiered on; Ahrons commented 'They had to be seen to be properly appreciated', and were distinguished by the venerable antiquity of their appearance. There was a sound reason for excluding third-class from the expresses, as the additional coaches would have overtaxed the Gooch singles. That was borne out when 3rd class passengers were graciously admitted to the *Jubilee*, a new train inaugurated to celebrate the Golden Jubilee of 1887. The load of the up train amounted to usually nine, sometimes eleven carriages, and the 8-footer required the assistance of a pilot, at least between Bristol and Swindon.

The last broad gauge 'Cornishman' to leave Paddington at 10.15 am on 20 May 1892 hauled by 8 ft single locomotive *Great Western*. Science Museum photograph.

Little has been said of goods trains but the demands made on the locomotives were less and in general their technology was less advanced than that of the fast passenger trains. As part of Gooch's initial building programme he had designed locomotives carried on six coupled wheels (0–6–0), similar to those built for goods traffic on other lines, but with some components that were common to the 'Firefly' class, the earliest example of standardisation in locomotive construction. The inside cylinder 0–6–0 handled nearly all goods traffic on British railways during the last century and much of it to the end of steam, with the improvements in general practice that affected all locomotives.

Meanwhile, the 8-ft singles held sway on the west of England trains, apparently for ever, but in February 1891 the Company took the decision to convert the final stretch and so finally to abolish the broad gauge. On double track

lines, as in South Wales, it had been possible to maintain a train service on one line while the other was worked on, but west of Exeter, of the 106 route miles of the main line, some 65 were single track. It was therefore decided to concentrate the entire work in the space of one weekend, 21–22 May 1892. The 1300 men from the Plymouth Engineering Division were augmented by 3400 brought in from other parts of the system. The weather was mercifully fine and the whole operation went according to the well-tried and meticulously worked-out plan. The last broad gauge train to Penzance left Paddington at 10.15 am on Friday, 20 May, reaching its destination at 8.20 pm. It began its return journey 50 minutes later, empty, collecting any broad gauge stock that remained as it wended its way east back to Swindon. At 5 pm, *Bulkeley*, one of the 1880 batch of singles, steamed out of Paddington with the last train of all to work down Brunel's old main line. At Bristol it came off and was replaced, appropriately enough, by *Iron Duke* itself. With that the broad gauge steamed into oblivion.[42] *Sic transit . . . .*

Other Gauges, in Britain and Abroad

The results of the gauge war came too late for some countries to profit from the British experience, but in time for others. Even so, railway gauge was still a debatable issue and the choice was affected by a variety of factors, from the unbridled laissez-faire of North America to, in India, the wisdom and far-sightedness of a single man in authority. The notes that follow are far from exhaustive and are intended merely to show the many ways in which the gauge problem was raised and tackled over the face of the globe.

The issue was wide open while the Great Western was under construction.

During the dark days of 1838, when Brunel seemed at times to fight a lone battle within the company, with at best lukewarm support from Wood, among a wider circle his innovations aroused considerable interest and even support. A 'friend to railways' observed: 'He has one half at least of the best engineers and mechanics in the country on his side; few at present agree as to the width desirable for the rails, but all are unanimous in the necessity of an increase'. The main reason was, as the *Railway Magazine* noted: 'Experience has shown, in the Liverpool and Manchester Railway, over and over again, that the rails are too narrow for the boiler-room they want; and that they would do much better if they had had a wider gauge. The Zarsko [i.e. Tsarskoe] Selo Railway [in Russia] has also been constructed upon a gauge of six feet, which we have been informed the engineer would on no account whatever change for the narrow gauge. On the point therefore of an increase of gauge, there can be no doubt. The difficulty is as to the extent of it, which is a question of experience to decide'.[43]

In Ireland, this very point had been reported on by the Irish Railway Commission, set up in 1836. The first public railway in Ireland was opened between Dublin and Kingstown (now Dun Laoghaire) in December 1834, to the 4 ft 8½ in. gauge. Attempts were then made on the more ambitious project of linking Dublin and Belfast, but these attempts foundered and development proceeded piecemeal. The Ulster Railway was authorised to construct a line from Belfast to Armagh, opened as far as Lisburn in 1839. The Commission had drawn up a comprehensive survey of the way railways should be developed in Ireland, and it recommended 'a uniform gauge for Ireland of 6 ft 2 in., which will have the effect of greatly reducing the friction, which by lowering the centre of gravity of the load the present vibratory motion of the carriages will be greatly diminished, and consequently also the wear and tear of both the carriages and of the line of way; advantages which it is presumed, will be cheaply purchased by a small addition to the first outlay'. The reasons for the broader gauge were very similar to those offered by Brunel, except that, with the carriage bodies about 6 ft in width, the Commission considered that a gauge of two inches wider would enable the bodies to be kept within the wheels. The Ulster Railway adopted this recommendation and accordingly laid the Belfast to Portadown section to this gauge.

But when the Dublin and Drogheda Railway began feeling its way in the direction of Belfast, it chose to disregard the Commission's recommended gauge and built to 5 ft 2 in. The Ulster Railway protested and Major-General Sir Charles Pasley, by that time, in 1841, Inspector General of Railways, was called in to adjudicate. He decided on 5 ft 3 in. and that has remained the Irish railway gauge ever since. The Ulster Railway, smarting under the decision, had to convert their line at a cost of £20 000, although two-thirds of this was met by compensation.[44]

In Scotland, too, there was a flirtation with wider gauges. The early wagonways had sported a variety from 4 ft to the standard. In 1839, the Arbroath and Forfar line was built to 5 ft 6 in., and so too was the Dundee and Arbroath. Thomas Grainger and John Miller proposed this gauge for the line from Glasgow to the Clyde coast but were prevailed upon to adopt the 'English standard'. As late as 1846, Miller was proclaiming to a select committee that 5 ft 6 in. or 6 ft was safer and should be made general, but he had to accept the general view and make the two lines just mentioned conform to the standard.[45]

In England, the land that originated the modern railway, there was less variation, on the main, steam-powered railways after 1830. Apart from the Great Western, the main exception to the Stephenson gauge was on the Eastern Counties Railway, incorporated in July, 1836. The engineer was John Braithwaite, whose earlier claim to fame was his association with the Swedish engineer John Ericsson, who submitted the unsuccessful *Novelty* locomotive at the Liverpool & Manchester locomotive trials of 1829. The directors of the Eastern Counties wanted a line on the grand scale of the Great Western, but Braithwaite would not run to 7 ft; be managed 5 ft, for curious reasons: 'With a little more space between the tubes we should have a more quiet action of the water in the boiler and consequently less ebullition, and therefore with my diagram and my section of my engine, I added to all its different bearings, and I added what I considered sufficient additional space to the tubes, the sum of which gave me four feet, eleven and three-quarters inches, and upon that I assumed that five feet would be about the thing'. The adjoining Northern &

Eastern line, out to Bishop's Stortford, also thought 5 ft to be 'about the thing', for it used the same tracks as the Eastern Counties as far as Stratford. But it was soon realised that they would suffer for standing out against the generality and only a year after the ECR was opened to Colchester in 1843, both lines were converted to standard gauge, at a cost of £1000 a mile. The locomotives were also converted and appeared none the worse for being deprived of Braithwaite's 'little more space'.[46]

On the Continent of Europe, the Stephenson gauge was all-pervasive, apart from isolated exceptions, such as the Basle to Strasbourg at 6 ft 3 in., the Baden State Railway at 5 ft 3 in. and the Ghent to Antwerp at 3 ft 9 in. True, on the periphery there were divergencies. Spain had established 5 ft 6 in. as the prevailing gauge by 1860, and Russia, after an initial foray into 6 ft, had fixed on 5 ft.

The first railway, between St. Petersburg and the Tsar's summer palace at Tsarskoe Selo, was on 6 ft gauge, while the second line to be authorised, between Warsaw and Vienna, was constructed to the 4 ft 8½ in. gauge. So when the Tsar set up a committee for the construction of the railway from St. Petersburg to Moscow, one of the questions that had to be decided was that of the gauge. Most of the committee members thought that 6 ft. should be adopted for much the same reasons as the broad gauge had been urged in Britain. But the American railway engineer, George Washington Whistler, who had been brought in as technical advisor to the committee, declared that 5 ft would meet the requirements equally well and his advice was accepted. (Whistler was father of the celebrated artist.)

It has sometimes been thought the different gauge was selected for strategic reasons and so *The Times* correspondent reported on 13 November 1866: 'The Russian Government, I am told, with a view to prevent an enemy advance into the country by rail, have adopted a slightly narrower [a mistake for wider] track than the one used on the rest of the Continent'. However, that seems not to have been the case; at the time the decision was made, the gauge of railways was still not a closed question. In fact, it proved easier for an invader to Russia to narrow the broad gauge track by relaying one rail than for the Russians to widen the gauge in occupied territory. For example, the Soviet attack on Warsaw in 1920 was hampered by the difference in gauges, but when the Poles advanced on Kiev they very quickly had through trains running from Poland into occupied territory.[47]

In North America, however, a wild confusion reigned for many years. Much of New England and some middle Atlantic states had adopted 4 ft 8½ in., not necessarily because they obtained their locomotives from England, since these could be built to a specified gauge. But further south-west, railway promotors thought in terms of short-haul transportation instead of a national network with a uniform gauge. Those who advocated uniformity went unheeded and a variety of widths from the standard up to 6 ft flourished all over the States and Canada. In the latter, the leading lines, such as the Great Western Railway of Canada, the St. Lawrence and Atlantic or the Grand Trunk, went for 5 ft 6 in. There were those who felt that a break of gauge at the US frontier was no bad thing, as it might prove a defence against US depredations. In the States too, breaks of gauge were not always looked on as disastrous. As Senator Grimes of Iowa observed: 'If I was controlled by any local interests, I should be in favour of break of gauge, because whenever there is a break in the gauge, there is always a large amount of business to be done, and a town immediately springs up around that place'. The conflict between such local interests and those interested in long-distance transhipment of goods assumed its most spectacular form with the Erie and North East Railroad, a 6 ft oasis in 4 ft 10 in. terrain. Legislation to force the line to narrow itself was forcibly resisted; the local mob tore up any converted track and the US Marshal sent to enforce the regulation found himself in the city jail. The citizens of Erie eventually conceded defeat, but only after having wrung heavy compensation from the rival interests. The Civil War underlined the military importance of uniformity and afterwards, the development of the grain traffic and internal commerce generally helped to convert the American railway scene from a conglomeration of small lines to a national network, over a period of 25 years or so.

The question of the gauge of the first transcontinental railway was referred by Congress to President Lincoln himself, who ruled in favour of the 5 ft of the Pacific Railroad in California. But standard gauge interests rallied support for a bill in Congress to have the ruling set aside and in 1863 they succeeded.

To mitigate the adverse effects of gauge breaks, various devices were tried. 'Compromise cars' were constructed, with wheel treads 5 in. wide, to run on tracks ranging from standard to 4 ft 10 in. Not surprisingly, this practice was stigmatised as 'questionable if not dangerous'. More sophisticated were the wheels sliding on axles, locked into position for gauges up to 5 ft. The trials were hailed as 'perfectly successful' and by the 1870s the Grand Trunk and

5 ft 6 in. gauge Bengal–Nagpur Railway 4–6–0 locomotive *Duke of Connaught*. Reproduced from M. Satow and R. Desmond, *Railways of the Raj*, 1980. Courtesy of Indian Railways Board and Solar Press.

its connecting lines had thousands of these vehicles. But in practice, defects in the equipment and its operation led to an alarming rise in the number of accidents. More satisfactory were the 'elevating machines' which raised the bodies of passenger and freight cars so that trucks of the appropriate gauge could be run beneath them. By 1880 these had become familiar sights to rail travellers. The arrangement was acceptable if traffic was light, as in the South, but as it took five or six minutes to change each car, severe delays built up where traffic was heavy. So the practice grew up in the 1870s of laying a third rail to enable standard gauge trains to run over broad gauge routes. This, as in England on the Great Western, proved to be the prelude to conversion to standard gauge.

While conversion was gathering pace in the 70s, a fresh distraction arose. It was the veritable fever of narrow gauge building, and stemmed from the paper given by Robert F. Fairlie in 1870 at the British Railway Association 'The gauge for the railways of the future'. Fairlie was advocating a gauge between 3 ft and 3 ft 6 in.; it was cheaper to construct and maintain, it was better suited to mountainous country because sharper curves were permissible. The railway world was split in two by the heated controversy that was generated by Fairlie's paper. The fever spread worldwide and in the US, by 1882, after a relatively short time, some 7000 miles of narrow gauge had been laid down.

Meanwhile, standard gauge was winning. Back in 1861, only 53% was standard, but by 1880, 81% could accommodate standard gauge trains, and most lines in Canada had conformed. The South held out for a while with 5 ft, but in 1886 came the great conversion of 13 000 miles of track in but two days, 31 May–1 June, after, of course, a great deal of preparatory work. Even then, the conversion was to 4 ft 9 in., not sufficiently different to prevent through working of standard stock, but still different. The odd half inch gradually disappeared and did not long survive the turn of the century. Canada meanwhile had become standard gauge territory by 1880.[48]

The chaos that reigned in North America could well have been matched in India. Schemes for railway development began to emerge in the 1840s, for lines striking into the interior from major ports. The first company to be incorporated, in 1849, was the splendidly named Great Indian Peninsula Railway, starting from Bombay. Meanwhile, on the eastern side, the Honourable Court of Directors of the East India Company, which enjoyed wide powers, had interest in the East Indian Railway from Calcutta, on the standard gauge. Development might have gone ahead piecemeal but for the arrival in India in January 1848 of a new governor-general: James Andrew Broun Ramsay, first Marquis of Dalhousie (1812–1860), not only the youngest, but perhaps the most able and far-sighted man to hold that position. As President of the Board of Trade in Peel's government, he had learnt much of railway matters and seen at close quarters the work of the Gauge Commission. He immediately brought his mind to bear on the railway situation in India and in 1850 drew up a detailed and rational report that firmly laid down guidelines for the future. Dalhousie may justly be hailed as the architect of the Indian railway system. He was able to impose his view of the role of government in railway development, as he had unsuccessfully tried to do in Britain: he enlisted private enterprise, 'directly but not vexatiously controlled by the government'. As to the gauge, he was most forthright, and his report is so clear and sensible on this vexed question that it is worth quoting at length:

'The Court of Directors have recommended at the same time the use of the narrow gauge of 4 ft 8½ in. for the railway about to be constructed. Although the letter of the Court recommends, but leaves to the Govt. of India to determine as to the gauge which should be adopted on this occasion, I consider the question to be one of such moment as to deserve careful consideration and an authoritative and conclusive decision by the highest authority connected with the Indian Empire; who alone can have access to that full in foundation and extended experience which would make such a decision really and satisfactorily conclusive.

The British legislature fell unconsciously and perhaps unavoidably into the mischievous error of permitting the introduction of two gauges into the United Kingdom. The numerous and grievous evils which arose from that permission are well known, and will long be felt throughout all England. The Govt. of India has in its power, and no doubt will carefully provide, that however widely the Railway system may be extended in this Empire in the time to come, these great evils shall be averted and that uniformity of gauge shall be rigidly enforced from the first. But I conceive that the Govt. should do more than this, and that now at the very outset of railway work it should not only determine that a uniform gauge shall be established in India, but that such uniform gauge shall be the one which science and experience may unite in selecting as the best.

At one time this question was much before me; and although I shall not myself attempt to offer an opinion on so vexed a question, yet I may venture to form one of the recorded views of men competent in every way to judge.

The evidence which was given before the gauge commission in 1846 and the evidence which has been given from time to time before the Committee of Parliament backed as it has been by very high authority abroad, is I venture to think, sufficient to show that the narrow gauge of 4 ft 8½ in. (a measurement adopted originally at haphazard and from the accident of local circumstances) is not the best gauge for the general purposes of a Railway; and that something intermediate between the narrow gauge of 4 ft 8½ in. and broad gauge of 7 feet will give greater advantage than belong to the former, and will substantially command all the benefits which are secured by the latter.'
The 'something intermediate' which he ordained was 5 ft 6 in., and so it came to pass.

By 1870, however, a network of feeder routes to the broad gauge main lines was being considered, and the much cheaper construction costs of the narrow gauge made it an attractive proposition. It was agreed that there should be a uniform narrow gauge, but no agreement as to whether it should be 2 ft 9 in. or 3 ft 6 in. Again the Governor-General, then Lord Mayo, came to the rescue and in a memorandum of 30 December 1870 ruled as follows: 'According to the best consideration I can give to this extremely difficult question, I recommend the adoption of a 3 ft 3 in. gauge'.

The deciding factor was strategic. In a vehicle on the metre gauge, two horses abreast could comfortably be carried, or a gun-carriage for the heaviest artillery.[49]

As in India, so in Australia was the railway gauge the consequence of the constitutional arrangements and of the personal characters of those involved. In Australia, there was no central authority such as a governor-general, and there was no-one like Dalhousie. Instead, each state went its own way, with unco-ordinated routes pressing inland from the various ports. The first line to be authorised in South Australia, in 1850 from Adelaide to Port Adelaide was on the 4 ft 8½ in. gauge, taking note of the earnest recommendation of the Colonial Secretary, Earl Grey, in a dispatch dated 30 June 1848.

Meanwhile, in the neighbouring state of New South Wales, the Sydney Railway Company was promoting several lines inland from Sydney. They appointed as engineer an Irishman named Shields who vigoruously advocated the Irish 5 ft 3 in. gauge. The Company was persuaded and sought the approval of the Colonial Office for this gauge. They agreed and the Act of 1852 incorporating the Company duly specified 5 ft 3 in. The states of Victoria and South Australia, not having so far committed themselves to purchase standard gauge equipment, fell into line. But the Sydney Company were running into difficulties, some of them with their lively engineer, and it was decided to reduce his pay. So he resigned and in his place came a Scottish engineer, Wallace, who was as firm in favour of the standard gauge as Shields had been for 5 ft 3 in. The State sought and obtained a repeal of their railway act to authorise the change, but Victoria and South Australia only heard of this when the measure came before their legislatures. They were incensed; their two small railway companies had already ordered rolling stock for the wider gauge. The states were quite independent of each other and the British Government did not see fit to impose uniformity at this stage, so they went their separate ways.

To the north, Queensland achieved independent status in 1859 and marked its spirit of independence, among various ways, in fixing the gauge of its first railway, opened in 1865, from Ipswich to Grandchester. The engineer, FitzGibbon,

Victorian Railways 5 ft 3 in. gauge *Albury Express* (left) running alongside 4 ft 8½ in. gauge *Spirit of Progress* train between Albury and Melbourne. Reproduced from C.C. Singleton and D. Burke, *Railways of Australia*, 1963. Courtesy of Angus & Robertson.

in the interests of economy in construction costs, particularly through the mountainous terrain he was going to have to contend with, chose a narrow gauge – 3 ft 6 in.

Later still, in Western Australia a few small privately-owned lines to serve the logging trade were opened, the first in 1871, with little thought of standardization, but by the mid-seventies the gauge here too settled down to 3 ft 6 in. The later gold finds led to an expansion and by the end of the century, there was a far greater mileage on this gauge, 5280, than the wider gauges, 2531 on 4 ft 8½ in. and 3615 on 5 ft 3 in. By this time, proposals were emerging for the formation of the Australian Commonwealth and earnest consideration was given to the unification of the railway network. But the estimated cost of conversion to standard gauge of £8 million was sufficient discouragement and the matter lapsed.

Australia's first 'Gloucester' was at Albury, on the border between New South Wales and Victoria, where passengers on the main route between Sydney and Melbourne had to change trains. It is still an interchange station, but through passengers now take the recently constructed standard gauge line, running alongside the original broad gauge from Albury to the outskirts of Melbourne. To overcome still further the effects of the sturdy but short-sighted independence of the early states, the 'Commonwealth', standard gauge line was constructed, first between Port Augusta and Kalgoorlie, opened in 1917. Its extension was

often urged but it was not until 1968 that the west coast of Perth was reached. Two years later, a new ocean-to-ocean service was inaugurated from Sydney to Perth on standard gauge throughout, using existing New South Wales metals, converted South Australian track and the trans-Australia line across Western Australia.[50]

As a final curiosity, we may note in passing an idea that would have raised even Brunel's eyebrows. During the 1939–45 war, Hitler's imagination was fired by a proposal for a line of colossal grandeur to link the western and eastern parts of conquered Europe, on a gauge of 4 metres. Hitler ordered detailed planning to start in May 1942 so that construction could proceed after the victory. The gauge was soon scaled down to a mere 3 m., but the scheme envisaged 1000 ton passenger trains travelling at 250 kph and 10 000 freight trains at 100 kph.

It would have been risky to suggest to the Führer that a line totally isolated from the vast standard gauge network on the Continent could have little economic justification, or that the standard gauge still had considerable scope for development, as the vast trains on USA metals had shown. So the project team worked away on the scheme, their efforts enshrined in a 10-volume report now in the East German archives at Potsdam. They doubtless worked in the firm belief and hope that the line would never be built and remain a figment of the Führer's warped imagination.[51]

Epilogue

In one corner of the world Brunel's 7 ft gauge lingered on. It stemmed from the early 1850s, when a 7 ft gauge line was constructed to carry stone from the quarry on Holyhead Mountain down to the harbour, originally for the construction of the breakwater. This gauge was chosen probably because the contractor had acquired locomotives and wagons used for the construction of the Great Western. In a mundane existence it had its moment of glory when Queen Victoria, Prince Albert and other members of the Royal Family took a journey on it on the occasion of their visit to Holyhead in 1853. Parts of the track survived until 1913, when they were converted to standard gauge.

One of the locomotives built for the line in 1861, an 0–4–0 tank, was sold to the harbour authorities of Ponta Delgada, the capital of the island of São Miguel in the Azores. Like the Liverpool & Manchester, the track was made to fit the locomotive and a length of broad gauge track came into existence to convey materials for the construction and repair of the harbour works. It was still there in 1983, surely the last surviving broad gauge line in the world.[52]

In Britain little was left to remind one of the broad gauge era, except perhaps the greater space than usual between down and up fast tracks on the old main line to Bristol, or the spacious platforms at Baker Street on the London underground. Of Gooch's locomotives only two escaped the scrap heap, the *North Star* and perhaps the most famous of the 8 ft singles, *Lord of the Isles*, built in 1850 and displayed at the Great Exhibition of 1851.[53] But in 1906 they were judged to be taking up too much space in Swindon Works and tragically they were broken up. Many of the components of *North Star* survived in a surprising variety of places and some were retrieved and incorporated in a full-size reproduction constructed for the Stockton & Darlington centenary celebrations in 1825. Of the 8-footers we happily now have a reminder of their former

magnificence in the full-size reproduction of *Iron Duke* commissioned by the Science Museum and completed in 1985. It recalls not only the superb concept of Brunel and the soundness of Gooch as a locomotive designer but also the turbulent controversies of a crucial period of railway development. The modern steam railway had been launched and main routes begun on the practical, cautious, rule-of-thumb methods inherited from the past. The time was ripe for someone, with a background and intellectual formation entirely different from those of the established engineers of the time, to take a fresh look at the problem and consider from first principles: what is the best way to build a railway? That someone was of course Brunel. There is always a risk that a system arrived at by that route may not in all points be justified in practice, but on the other hand, without it, rule-of-thumb practice can become

Broad gauge locomotives at Swindon awaiting scrapping 1892. Courtesy of British Rail, Western Region.

mediocre and even stagnate. So the broad gauge system provided a very necessary stimulus enabling railway practice to develop much faster than it would otherwise have done, to the benefit of shareholder and travelling public alike.

In 1835, Brunel proposed to his company a system that offered great advantages at relatively small additional cost and given the state of the railway art at the time and the direction in which future development must have appeared to be moving, it was not unreasonable for the company to decide in its favour. After the opening in 1841, it must also have appeared, thanks to the excellence of Brunel's road and the indispensable help of Gooch, as though the decision were vindicated. But within a very few years, as the rail network linked up a tightly-knit community, the commercial disadvantages of standing alone should have become obvious. Conversion to standard gauge in, say, 1844

of about 250 route miles, without the expense of mixed gauge, would have been far cheaper than 'pressing on regardless', which, being by now committed to the system, they decided to do. So the verdict of L.T.C. Rolt, Brunel's biographer, really sums up the matter: the broad gauge was an engineering triumph but a costly commercial mistake.

One final point is worth considering. Any organisation that provides goods or services needs the following of a clientele, the good-will of a body of potential customers. In this, the Great Western broad gauge was curiously and supremely successful. Its passing in 1892 was genuinely and generally mourned in the West Country. It had become a much-loved institution. When *Iron Duke* pulled out of Bristol on its last journey, crowds assembled to watch its progress, in silent tribute as if for the passing of a national hero.

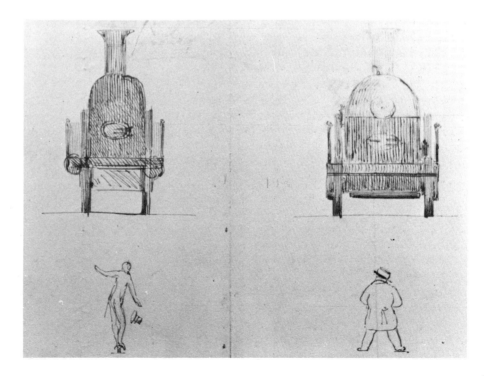

Broad and narrow – men and machines. Drawing by C.A. Saunders in the Great Western Museum, Swindon.

Notes and References

1 Charles E. Lee, *The evolution of railways*, 2nd ed., London: The Railway Gazette, 1943, for the early development of railway track and gauge.

2 Charles E. Lee, 'The "railways" of Ancient Greece', *Railway Magazine*, 1941, vol. 87, pp 53–4.

3 R.H.G. Thomas, *The Liverpool & Manchester Railway*, London: B.T. Batsford, 1980, especially p. 59.

4 L.T.C. Rolt, *Isambard Kingdom Brunel: a biography*, London: Longmans, Green and Co., 1957, pp. 44–5 for Brunel's first railway journey and pp. 66–186 for the early history of the Great Western Railway and especially Brunel's part in it.

5 The classic history is E.T. MacDermot, *History of the Great Western Railway*, 2 vol., London: 1927–1931; revised edition by C.R. Clinker, 2 vol., Ian Allan, 1964, Indispensable source in this field, used throughout this study.

6 H. Pollins, 'A note on railway constructional costs 1825–1850', *Economica*, 1962, ns vol. 19, pp. 395–407.

7 House of Lords parchment collection, 23 July 1834. Both editions of E.T. MacDermot, *op. cit.*, state that 'no copy of this Bill seems to have survived', but that is not so.

8 *An act for making a railway from Bristol to join the London and Birmingham Railway near London, to be called "Great Western Railway", with Branches therefrom to the Towns of Bradford and Trowbridge in the County of Wilts*, 31st August 1835. House of Lords Record Office parchment collection, printed in *Local and Personal Acts*, 5 & 6 W IV, cap. cvii.

9 Brunel first referred to the broad gauge in his first report to the GWR Board dated 14 September 1835 and urged the case for it in his second report dated the following day, in *Brunel's reports to the Great Western Railway Board 1835–1842*, Public Record Office RAIL 250/82. The second report is printed in full in MacDermot, *op. cit.*, 1964, pp. 17–19.

10 N. Wood, *A practical treatise on rail-roads*, 3rd ed., London: Longman, Orme, Brown, Green & Longmans, [1838], pp. 713–9.

11 *Railway Magazine*, 1838, ns vol. 5, p. 17.

12 T.A. Britton, *A treatise on the origin, progress, preservation and cure of dry rot in timber*, London: E. & F.N. Spon, 1875, pp. 125–6.

13 Brunel's report to the Board dated 26 January 1837, PRO RAIL 259/82.

14 *The Times*, 5 June 1838, p. 5.

15 Gooch's description in D. Gooch, *Memoirs & diary, transcribed . . . and edited by R.B. Wilson*, Newton Abbot: David & Charles, 1972, p. 31.

16 *Railway Magazine*, 1838, ns vol. 5, pp. 15ff.

17 D. Gooch, *op. cit.*, p. 28.

18 *The Times*, 8 June 1838, p. 6.

19 *Railway Magazine*, 1838, ns vol. 5, p. 377.

20 (*Reports to the Directors of the Great Western Railway by John Hawkshaw, I.K. Brunel and Nicholas Wood*], 5 pt., London: [1838]. Extensively reprinted with observations by the editor, in *Railway Magazine*, 1839, ns vol. 5, pp. 631–62.

21 D. Gooch, *op. cit.*, pp. 38–9.

22 *Railway Magazine*, 1839, ns vol. 5, pp. 644ff.

23 T. Mackay, *The Life of Sir John Fowler*, London: John Murray, 1900, pp. 31–4.

24 *Railway Magazine*, 3 July 1841, p. 569.

25 H. Pollins, *op. cit.*, p. 407.

26 Brunel's estimates of the additional work and expense entailed occur in his reports to the GWR Board of 15 September 1838 and 13 July 1838 in Public Record Office

RAIL 259/82. Brunel and other engineers were examined on this point by the Gauge Commissioners, and their replies are recorded in *Minutes of evidence taken before the Commissioners*, London; 1846. Widths of various works, such as cuttings, embankments and tunnels, on 41 railways are given in *Gauge Commissioners' Report: Appendix consisting of . . . statistical returns*, etc., London: 1846, pp. 347ff.

27 R. M. Stephenson, *Rudimentary and practical instructions on the science of railway construction*, London: John Weale, 1861, pp. 70ff.

28 R. M. Stephenson, *op. cit.*, p. 180.

29 [F.R. Conder], *Personal recollections of English engineers*, London, Hodder and Stroughton, 1868, reprinted as *The men who built railways*, edited by J. Simmons, London: Thomas Telford, 1983, pp. 118ff.

30 *Oxford, Worcester and Wolverhampton Railway, and Oxford and Rugby Railway Bills, reports of Committees*, London: 1845.

31 *The Times*, 8 July 1845.

32 *Report of the Gauge Commissioners, presented to both Houses of Parliament*, London: 1846 (The Report pp. 4–31, appendix of data pp. 22–7); *Minutes of evidence taken before the Commissioners*, London: 1846, pp. [i–iv], 1–346; Appendix consisting of supplementary replies to questions, and statistical returns, together with an account of the experiments made under the sanction of the Commissioners . . . London: 1846, pp. [1–ii], 347–818.

33 Many are listed in G. Ottley, *A bibliography of British railway history*, London: George Allen & Unwin, 1965 [i.e. 1966]; 2nd ed., London: HMSO, 1983; supplement volume in press.

34 *Observations on the Report of the Gauge Commissioners*, Westminster: 1846; *Supplemental observations on the published evidence and appendix of the Gauge Commissioners*, Westminster: 1846.

35 9 & 10 Vict. cap. 57, reprinted in J. Bigg, *General railway acts*, London: many editions, e.g. 12th ed., 1866.

36 L.T.C. Rolt, *op. cit.*, p. 112.

37 Information from the tables of E.T. MacDermot, *op. cit.*, 1964, vol. 1, appendix I. In all, 1232 miles of broad gauge were laid, the final stretch being the 4¼ mile branch to St. Ives in 1877, apart from a few chains opened in Plymouth Harbour in 1879. But the mileage of broad gauge in operation began to decline after the conversion programme got under way. *See* C.R. Clinker, *New light on the gauge controversy*, Bristol: Avon Anglia Publications & Services, 1978.

38 O.S. Nock, *The Great Western Railway in the nineteenth century*, London: Ian Allan, 1962, pp. 149ff.; C. Moggs, 'Conversion to standard-gauge [of the Bath to Weymouth line]', *Locomotive papers*, 19, no. 138; E.T. MacDermot, *op. cit.*, 1964, vol. 2, pp. 196ff.

38a Dean reported these figures in July 1892 (E.T. MacDermot, *op. cit.*, 1964, vol. 2, p 202), although slightly different figures are given in other sources.

39 S.R. Yates, 'The broad gauge 8-ft "Singles" of the Great Western Railway', *Railway Magazine*, 1931, vol. 69, pp. 391–9.

		"Iron Duke" 1847	"Tornado" 1888
Cylinders—			
Diameter	.. ..	18 in.	18 in.
Stroke	.. ..	24 in.	24 in.
Heating Surface—			
Firebox	.. sq. ft.	147·9	137·0
Tubes	.. "	1797·1	1947·7
Total	.. "	1945·0	2084·7
Grate Area	.. "	21·7	24·0
Weight of Engine	..	35 t. 10 c.	41 t. 8 c.
Wheel Base of Engine	..	18 ft 6 in.	19 ft 0 in.
Leading and Trailing Wheels		4 ft 6 in.	4 ft 6 in.

The boiler pressure was originally $100\,lb/in^2$, later raised to $115\,lb/in^2$. Locomotives rebuilt or built new after 1870 had boilers at $140\,lb/in^2$ pressure.

40 G. Reder, *The world of steam locomotives*, tr. from German, London: Blandford Press, 1974, pp. 86ff.

41   E.L. Ahrons, *Locomotive and train working in the latter half of the nineteenth century*, vol. 4, Cambridge: W. Heffer, 1953; reprinted articles in *Railway Magazine*, 1915–1923.

42   *Railway News*, 28 May 1892, pp. 839–40; *Great Western Magazine*, 1892, vol. 4, pp. 85–6.

43   *Railway Magazine*, 1837, ns vol. 3, p. 13; 1838, ns vol. 5, p. 18.

44   H.C. Casserley, *Outline of Irish Railway History*, Newton Abbot: David & Charles, 1974; *Second report of the Commissioners appointed to consider and enquire into a general system of railways for Ireland*, (Reports from Commissioners, XXXV, 1837–1838), London, 1838; summarized in *Railway Magazine*, 1838, vol. 5; E.M. Patterson, *The Great Northern Railway of Ireland*, Lingfield: Oakwood Press, 1962, pp. 6–7.

45   C.J.A. Robertson, *The origins of the Scottish railway system*, Edinburgh: John Donald, 1983, pp. 17, 124, 194.

46   C. Hamilton Ellis, *British railway history*, vol. 1, London: George Allen & Unwin, 1954, pp. 87ff. based on S. Sidney, *Gauge evidence*, London: 1846, pp. 1ff.

47   J.N. Westwood, *History of Russian railways*, London: George Allen & Unwin, 1964, pp. 30–1.

48   G.R. Taylor & I.D. Neu, *The American railroad network, 1861–1890*, Cambridge, Mass.: 1956.

49   O.S. Nock, *Railways of Asia and the Far East*, London: Adam and Charles Black, 1978.

50   O.S. Nock, *Railways of Australia*, London: Adam and Charles Black, 1971.

51   M. Robbins, 'Hitler's broad gauge railway: a review article', *J. Transp. Hist.*, 1983, ns *4* (1), 67–73.

52   *Railway Magazine*, July 1961, pp. 468–9.

53   In 1927 a diminutive broad gauge locomotive on four wheels came to light in the works at Newton Abbot and *Tiny* graced a station platform there for many years. It is now in the Dart Valley Railway Museum at Buckfastleigh.

Printed in the UK for HMSO
Dd 736289   C50   4/85